LECTINS

LECTINS

N. Sharon
and
H. Lis

Department of Biophysics
The Weizmann Institute of Science
Rehovot, Israel

LONDON NEW YORK
CHAPMAN AND HALL

First published in 1989 by
Chapman and Hall Ltd
11 New Fetter Lane, London EC4P 4EE

Published in the USA by
Chapman and Hall
29 West 35th Street, New York NY 10001

Typeset in 10/12 pt Sabon by Thomson Press (India) Limited, New Delhi

Printed and bound in Great Britain at the University Press, Cambridge

ISBN 0 412 27380 2

British Library Cataloguing in Publication Data

Sharon, Nathan
Lectins
1. Lectins
I. Title
574.19'245
ISBN 0-412-27380-2

Library of Congress Cataloging in Publication Data

Sharon, Nathan.
Lectins/Nathan Sharon and Halina Lis.
p. cm.
Bibliography: p.
Includes index.
ISBN 0-412-27380-2
1. Lectins. I. Lis, Halina, 1923- .II. Title.
[DNLM: 1. Lectins. QW 640 S531L]
QP552.L42S53 1989
574.19'245--dc 19
DNLM/DLC
for Library of Congress

88-39044
CIP

Contents

Acknowledgements viii

1 **Introduction** 1

2 **History** 6
- 2.1 The early pioneers 6
- 2.2 What's in a name? 11
- 2.3 Into the limelight 14
- 2.4 A tool for cancer research 16
- 2.5 Rekindling of interest 17
- 2.6 Insight into biological functions 18
- 2.7 Into contemporary lectin research 19

3 **Occurrence and isolation** 20
- 3.1 Occurrence 21
- 3.2 Isolation 24

4 **Biological activities** 26
- 4.1 Cell agglutination 26
- 4.2 Mitogenic stimulation of lymphocytes 27
- 4.3 Lectin mediated killing of animal target cells 32
- 4.4 Phagocytosis of yeasts and bacteria 33
- 4.5 Insulin-like activity 33
- 4.6 Cytotoxicity 33
- 4.7 Nutritional aspects 34

5 **Carbohydrate specificity** 37
- 5.1 Monosaccharides 40
- 5.2 Oligosaccharides 42

6 **Molecular properties** 47
6.1 Subunit structure 47
6.2 Isolectins 48
6.3 Metals in lectins 50
6.4 Lectins as glycoproteins 51
6.5 Primary structures and homologies 52

7 **Three dimensional structures** 59
7.1 Legume lectins 59
7.2 Wheat germ agglutinin 61
7.3 Ricin 62
7.4 Influenza virus haemagglutinin 63

8 **Biosynthesis** 65

9 **Applications** 69
9.1 Glycoconjugates in solution 70
9.2 Membrane bound sugars 76
9.3 Mapping neuronal pathways 84
9.4 Cell separation 85
9.5 Lectins in microbiological studies 86
9.6 Clinical uses 87
9.7 Lectins in space biology 90

10 **Lectin resistant cells** 92
10.1 Glycosylation pathways 93
10.2 Functions of cell surface sugars 95

11 **Functions in nature** 97
11.1 In plants 98
11.2 In vertebrate animals 100
11.3 In invertebrates 103
11.4 In slime molds 104
11.5 In parasites 105
11.6 In bacteria 106
11.7 In viruses 107

12 **Epilogue** 108

References 109

Appendix A: Molecular properties of some purified lectins 115

Appendix B: Systematic and common names 119

Index 121

Acknowledgements

We wish to thank our many friends and colleagues for their advice and suggestions during the preparation of this book. Our special appreciation is due to Michael Edidin, R. Colin Hughes, Frank L. Loontiens, Samuel H. Barondes and Jonathan M. Gershoni. We are also thankful to Dvorah Ochert for her expert secretarial and editorial assistance.

CHAPTER 1
Introduction

A characteristic property of most, or perhaps all, proteins is their ability to combine specifically and reversibly with various substances. Well known examples are enzymes that bind substrates and inhibitors, and antibodies that bind antigens. This book deals with lectins, a class of proteins that bind carbohydrates. Another characteristic property of lectins is that they agglutinate cells or precipitate polysaccharides and glycoproteins. This is because lectins are polyvalent, i.e. each lectin molecule has at least two carbohydrate binding sites to allow crosslinking between cells (by combining with sugars on their surfaces) or between sugar containing macromolecules. The agglutinating and precipitating activities of lectins are very similar to those of antibodies. They can likewise be specifically inhibited by low molecular weight compounds (haptens), which in the case of lectins are sugars or sugar containing compounds (Fig. 1.1). Not surprisingly, therefore, many of the methods used in lectin research are based on immunochemical techniques.

Nevertheless, lectins are different from antibodies in several important aspects. Many lectins are found in plants, microorganisms and viruses, which do not synthesize immunoglobulins. In fact, they are found in almost all living organisms (Table 1.1) and are not confined to specific organs or tissues. Another marked difference between the two classes of compound is that antibodies are structurally similar, whereas lectins are structurally diverse. In general, lectins are oligomeric proteins composed of subunits, usually with one sugar binding site per subunit. They vary, however, in molecular size, amino acid composition, metal requirement, and three dimensional structure. In their structural diversity, lectins are akin to enzymes, but they are devoid of catalytic activity. In spite of this variation, they can be grouped in families of structurally homologous proteins, the best characterized of which is that of the legume lectins.

The ability to bind carbohydrates is not confined to lectins. Other sugar binding proteins include the many enzymes, such as kinases, mutases, glycosidases and transferases, that participate in carbohydrate metabolism, as well as the proteins involved in active transport of sugars. As a rule, however, these proteins contain only one carbohydrate binding site per molecule and, therefore, do not agglutinate cells.

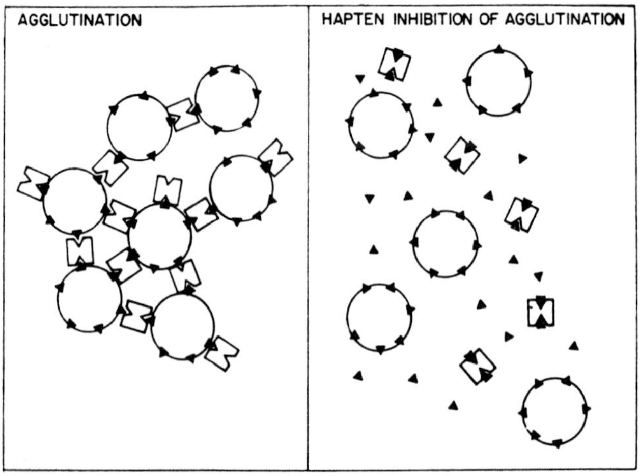
AGGLUTINATION
HAPTEN INHIBITION OF AGGLUTINATION

Fig. 1.1 Schematic representation of cell agglutination by a lectin and of hapten inhibition of the agglutination. Cells are represented by circles with solid triangles, the latter denoting cell surface sugars. The hapten inhibitor is represented by free solid triangles. Interaction of the hapten with the lectin prevents cell agglutination. (Reproduced with permission from Herschman, H.R. (1972) In *Membrane Molecular Biology* (eds C.F. Fox and A.D. Keith), Sinauer Associates, Stanford, pp. 471–502.)

Lectins are classified into a small number of specificity groups (mannose*, galactose, *N*-acetylglucosamine, *N*-acetylgalactosamine, L-fucose and *N*-acetylneuraminic acid) according to the monosaccharide which is the most effective inhibitor of the agglutination of erythrocytes precipitation of carbohydrate polymers by the lectin (Table 1.1). A striking feature of the monosaccharides listed in Table 1.1 is that they are all constituents of animal glycoconjugates and are also present on surfaces of cells, including erythrocytes. Lectins specific for other sugars have very rarely been encountered. This may be a reflection of the method routinely employed for the detection of lectins, which is agglutination of erythrocytes – haemagglutination in brief.

Although lectins have been known for nearly a century, they have become the focus of intense interest only during the last decade or two. This is evident from the rapid growth of the literature on the subject, which since the 1960s has increased about 20-fold: the total number of publications that deal with various aspects of lectins is fast approaching 2000 per year. There are many reasons for the current interest in lectins. Prominent among these is their usefulness in detecting and studying carbohydrates in solution and on cell surfaces. In addition, investigations of the interaction of lectins with carbohydrates are providing information on the precise molecular details of the reactions between proteins and carbohydrates in general, as well as between cells. Lectins serve as invaluable tools in biological and medical research, in areas as diverse as separation and characterization of

*All sugars are of the D configuration unless otherwise noted.

Table 1.1 Distribution of lectins in nature*

	Source of lectin			
Sugar specificity	*Plants*	*Vertebrates*	*Invertebrates*	*Microorganisms and viruses*
Mannose	Fava bean	Rat liver		*Escherichia coli*
	Jack bean			*Klebsiella pneumoniae*
	Lentil			
	Pea			
Galactose	Castor bean	Electric eel	Beetle	Amoeba
	Erythrina cristagalli	Human placenta	Flesh fly	*Pseudomonas aeruginosa*
	Griffonia simplicifolia	Rabbit liver	Sea urchin	Slime mold
	Peanut	Snake venom		
N-Acetylglucosamine	*Griffonia simplicifolia*	Chicken liver		
	Ulex europaeus			
	Wheat			
N-Acetylgalactosamine	*Dolichos biflorus*		Garden snail	
	Lima bean		Cockroach	
	Soybean			
L-Fucose	*Lotus tetragonolobus*	Eel serum		*Vibrio cholerae*
	Ulex europeaus	Rat liver		
N-Acetylneuraminic acid	Elderberry	Frog	Horseshoe crab	Influenza virus
	Wheat		Lobster	*Mycoplasma gallisepticum*
			Slug	

*For plants and animals that are usually referred to by their common rather than by their systematic names, the former will be preferred throughout the text. A list of both types of name is given in Appendix A.

glycoproteins and glycopeptides, histochemistry of cells and tissues, cell differentiation, tracing neuronal pathways, typing of bacteria and fractionation of lymphocytes and of bone marrow cells for bone marrow transplantation. They are also employed to stimulate lymphocytes in assessing the immune state of patients, for chromosome analysis in human cytogenetics, as well as for the production of lymphokines.

As our knowledge about lectins expanded, it became apparent that they deserved attention in their own right: some of them consist of polypeptides with rare structural features, or are glycoproteins with unusual carbohydrate units. Studies of the molecular genetics of lectins have provided insight into novel controls of gene expression. Furthermore, the occurrence of lectins in different tribes, species or genera of the same family make them suitable objects for taxonomic and phylogenetic studies, as well as for evolutionary correlations. The extensive homologies observed between lectins from taxonomically related sources demonstrate that these proteins have been conserved throughout evolution and provide strong evidence that they must have an important function (or functions) in nature.

Little is known with certainty about these functions, but it is generally believed that lectins serve primarily as recognition determinants. The haemagglutinin of the influenza virus binds to sialic acid containing receptors on the surface of target cells, thus initiating the virus–cell interaction. Surface lectins of bacteria and of intestinal parasites, such as the amoeba, mediate the sugar specific adherence of the organisms to epithelial cells, e.g. in the gastrointestinal or urinary tracts, and thus facilitate infection. The bacterial lectins also mediate the attachment to sugar residues on phagocytic cells, and permit the latter to kill the bacteria in the absence of serum factors, in a process designated lectinophagocytosis. Plant lectins have been implicated in mediating attachment of symbiotic nitrogen fixing bacteria to the roots of leguminous plants and in the protection of plants against fungal phytopathogens. In animals, membrane associated lectins appear to function in the clearance of glycoproteins from the circulatory system, in directing glycoproteins to different organelles within the cell, in the migration of recirculating lymphocytes from the blood stream to lymph nodes, spleen and other lymphoid organs and in the process of metastasis.

Contributing to the increasing popularity of lectins is their ease of purification, mainly by affinity chromatography on immobilized carbohydrates. Indeed, well over 100 lectins have been obtained in purified form and characterized to a considerable extent (see Appendix A) and this number is growing fast. Many of them are available from commercial sources, either in their native form or as derivatives. The latter include fluorescent lectins widely used in microscopic studies and immobilized lectins for the separation and characterization of oligosaccharides and glycoproteins.

The purpose of this book is to give an overview of the properties of lectins, their applications in biology and medicine and their possible functions. For more detailed information, the reader is referred to a recent comprehensive treatise on the subject [1] as well as other recent books and reviews [2–5a]. These also provide access to the earlier literature on lectins. References given in the text are predominantly to very recent publications not mentioned in these sources. Since the subject of lectins is intimately linked to that of carbohydrates, readers may find it helpful to consult the book *Glycoproteins* by R. Colin Hughes in the Outline Studies in Biology Series [6].

CHAPTER 2
History

A survey of the history of lectins is of interest since it gives insight into the development of an area of research that has wide implications and is of increasing importance; it also serves as an appropriate introduction to the discussion of some of the outstanding properties of these proteins (Table 2.1). Like the histories of many areas of research, this one too is rich in examples of chance and serendipity [7, 8].

2.1 THE EARLY PIONEERS

Lectins were first designated as 'haemagglutinins', or more commonly as 'phytohaemagglutinins', because they were found almost exclusively in plants. The earliest report of the occurrence in plants of proteins which agglutinate human or animal erythrocytes appeared in 1888 in the doctoral thesis of Hermann Stillmark (Fig. 2.1), a student of Robert Kobert at the University of Dorpat, in Estonia (now Tartu in the USSR), one of the oldest universities in Czarist Russia [8a]. Stillmark was studying the toxicity of castor beans (*Ricinus communis*)* but finding his conscience troubled by the suffering of the animals in his experiments he chose to work *in vitro*. Mixing an extract of the beans with blood, he made the startling observation that the erythrocytes were agglutinated. He further showed that the material causing the agglutination was a protein, and gave it the name 'ricin'. Shortly afterwards, H. Hellin, also a student of Kobert, discovered that the toxic extract of the jequirity bean (*Abrus precatorius*) also caused the red cells to clump together. The new agglutinin was named 'abrin'.

These reports immediately attracted the attention of Paul Ehrlich (Fig. 2.2) at the Royal Institute for Experimental Therapy, Frankfurt. He realized that the plant agglutinins would be more useful model antigens for the solution of immunological

*The systematic and common names of the organisms mentioned in this book are listed in Appendix B. Unless the organisms are better known by their systemic names, their common names will be used.

Table 2.1 Milestones in lectin research

Year	*Scientists*	*Event*
1888	Stillmark	Haemagglutinating activity in extracts of castor beans
1891	Ehrlich	Use of ricin and abrin for immunological research
1908	Landsteiner and Raubitschek	Species specificity of plant haemagglutinins
1919	Sumner	Isolation and crystallization of concanavalin A
1936	Sumner and Howell	Sugar specificity of concanavalin A
1948–9	Renkonen; Boyd and Reguera	Blood group specificity of plant lectins
1952	Morgan and Watkins	Demonstration with the aid of lectins that sugars are determinants of blood group specificity
1960	Nowell	Mitogenic stimulation of lymphocytes by phytohaemagglutinin (PHA)
1963	Aub *et al.*	Preferential agglutination of malignant cells by wheat germ agglutinin
1965	Goldstein *et al.*	Concanavalin A purified by affinity chromatography Structural studies of carbohydrates with concanavalin A
1968	Burger; Inbar and Sachs	Preferential agglutination of malignant cells by concanavalin A
1970	Aspberg, Lloyd and Porath	Use of concanavalin A for affinity purification of glycoproteins
1970–1	Powell and Leon; Novogrodsky and Katchalski	Mitogenic stimulation of lymphocytes by concanavalin A
1972	Edelman *et al*; Hardman and Ainsworth	Primary and three dimensional structure of concanavalin A
1974	Ashwell and Morell	Role of animal lectins in endocytosis of glycoproteins
1976	Gallo	Interleukin 2 discovered in medium of PHA stimulated lymphocytes
1976	Reisner and Sharon	Fractionation of mouse thymocytes by peanut agglutinin and of mouse splenocytes by soybean agglutinin
1977	Ofek, Mirelman and Sharon	Bacterial lectins play a role in infection
1981	Reisner *et al.*	Use of soybean agglutinin for bone marrow transplantation

Fig. 2.1 Hermann Stillmark (1860–1923). (Courtesy of Prof. Dr H. Franz).

Fig. 2.2 Paul Ehrlich (1854–1915). (Reproduced with permission from the Wellcome Institute Library, London.)

problems than the bacterial toxins, such as that of diphtheria, which were popular research tools at the time. They were much easier to prepare in large quantities than bacterial antigens, and were also much more stable. What was more important, when injected into animals ricin or abrin stimulated the production of antibodies that inhibited both their toxic and agglutinating activities, thereby facilitating their study in the test tube. Although Ehrlich's preparations were very crude by present day criteria (we now know that both the 'ricin' and 'abrin' were mixtures of a weakly agglutinating protein toxin and a non-toxic agglutinin), he was able to establish with them some of the fundamental principles of immunology. Ehrlich found that mice were rendered immune to a lethal dose of ricin or abrin by repeated small (sublethal), subcutaneous injections of the lectin, and that anti-ricin did not protect the animals against the toxic effects of abrin, nor did anti-abrin protect against ricin. This provided clear evidence for the specificity of the immune response. Ehrlich also showed that immunity to the toxins was transferred from a mother to her offspring by blood during pregnancy and by milk after birth. By studying the inhibitory effect of the anti-ricin immune serum on the agglutinating activity of ricin, he demonstrated that there was a quantitative relationship between the amount of antiserum and the amount of antigen it could neutralize, and on this basis performed the first quantitative determination of an antibody *in vitro*.

The sugar specificity of lectins was discovered in 1936 by James B. Sumner

Fig. 2.3 James B. Sumner (1887–1955).

(Fig. 2.3) from Cornell University, Ithaca, New York, who is well known for being the first to crystallize an enzyme, urease, from jack bean (*Canavalia ensiformis*), a feat he achieved in 1926. Prior to that, in 1919, he isolated a protein which he named concanavalin A from the jack bean by salt precipitation and, crystallization, thus obtaining for the first time a pure lectin. Together with S.F. Howell, he reported in 1936 that in addition to its ability to agglutinate cells such as erythrocytes and yeasts, concanavalin A also precipitated glycogen from solution. They further showed that haemagglutination by concanavalin A was inhibited by cane sugar and, with much foresight, suggested that this might be the consequence of a reaction of the plant protein with carbohydrates on the surface of the red cells.

Already the early results obtained by Stillmark indicated some selectivity in the lectin mediated agglutination of red cells from different animals. This observation was corroborated and further extended by Karl Landsteiner the discoverer of blood groups (Fig. 2.4), working at the Rockefeller Institute in New York together with H. Raubitschek. They demonstrated in 1908 that the relative haemagglutinating activities of various seed extracts were quite different when tested with red blood cells from different animals. For instance, pea extracts were very effective in agglutinating rabbit erythrocytes but far less effective with sheep or pigeon erythrocytes, whereas human red blood cells were strongly agglutinated by bean extracts and weakly agglutinated by pea or lentil extracts. Because of this specificity, Landsteiner concluded that the reactions of plant haemagglutinins

Fig. 2.4 Karl Landsteiner (1868–1943). (Reproduced with permission from The Rockefeller Archive Center.)

'resemble antibody reactions in all essentials'. He therefore used both classes of protein in the discussion of specificity in the introductory chapter of his classic book *The Specificity of Serological Reactions*, first published in 1936.

2.2 WHAT'S IN A NAME?

In the late 1940s, William C. Boyd (Fig. 2.5) and Rose M. Reguera from Boston University and, independently, Karl O. Renkonen (Fig. 2.6) from the University of Helsinki, Finland, reported that certain seeds contain agglutinins specific for some human blood group antigens. Boyd described his discovery in a lecture he gave at a Landsteiner centennial symposium held in New York in 1970. He related how one day, toward the end of 1945, looking at the table in Landsteiner's book showing that plant extracts do not always agglutinate the blood of different species equally

> I was seized with the idea that if such extracts could show species specificity, they might even show individual specificity; that is, they might possibly affect the red cells of some individuals of a species and not affect others of the same species. Therefore I asked one of my assistants to go out to the corner grocery store and buy some dried lima beans. Why I said lima beans instead of the more common pea beans or kidney beans, I shall never know. But if we had bought practically any other bean we would not have discovered anything new.

Fig. 2.5 William C. Boyd (1904–1983).

Fig. 2.6 Karl O. Renkonen (1905–1986).

Indeed, when the lima beans (*Phaseolus limensis* or *Phaseolus lunatus*) were ground and extracted with salt solution, the resulting extracts agglutinated only human erythrocytes of blood type A and not of blood types B or O.

> The ease with which this discovery was made misled me, and aside from a rather oblique reference to it in the second edition of my *Fundamentals of Immunology* (1947), which I was working on at that time, I did not publish this observation until 1949, when I reported on an investigation of 262 varieties of plants belonging to 63 families and 186 genera.

In 1948, Renkonen reported his independent study of 57 species belonging to 28 genera. They included the common vetch, *Vicia cracca*, the extract of which was specific for the blood group A antigen, and certain other seed extracts, notably that of the asparagus pea, *Lotus tetragonolobus*, specific for the blood group O antigen. Olavi Mäkelä, a student of Renkonen, described in his Ph.D. thesis, published in 1957, results of an investigation of extracts from seeds representing 743 plant species and 165 genera, all of the family Leguminosae. He found haemagglutinating activity in more than one third of them; close to one in ten exhibited blood group specificity. Interestingly, although several of the latter were either O, A or both A and B type specific, only one, that from *Griffonia simplicifolia*, (also known as *Bandeiraea simplicifolia*), exhibited almost exclusively B type specificity. Since then, additional lectins specific for blood types A and O have been discovered, as well as several specific for other blood groups. Thus, seeds of *Vicia graminea* were found in 1953 to react specifically with erythrocytes of blood type N, and not with those of type M. However, no new B type specific lectins have been found.

The blood group specificity of some lectins is so sharply defined that they can distinguish between blood subgroups. The lectin of the legume horse gram, *Dolichos biflorus*, for example, reacts more strongly with red cells of type A_1 than with those of type A_2, as first shown by George W.G. Bird from Birmingham in 1951.

The ability of plant agglutinins to distinguish between erythrocytes of different blood types led Boyd and Elizabeth Shapleigh in 1954 to propose for them the name 'lectins', from the Latin *legere*, to pick out or choose. This name has superseded all earlier designations such as phytoagglutinin or phytohaemagglutinin, and is now used for all sugar binding, cell agglutinating proteins of non-immune origin, whether from plants, animals or microorganisms.

The blood type specific lectins played a crucial role in the early investigations on the chemical basis of the specificity of the antigens associated with the ABO and Lewis blood group systems. Walter J.T. Morgan and Winifred M. Watkins (Fig. 2.7), working in the early 1950s at the Lister Institute, London, showed that the agglutination of type A red cells by the lima bean lectin was inhibited best by α-linked *N*-acetylgalactosamine, and that of type O cells by the lectin of *Lotus tetragonolobus* was inhibited best by α-linked L-fucose. They thus demonstrated

Fig. 2.7 Walter J.T. Morgan (b. 1900) and Winifred M. Watkins (b. 1924).

for the first time that the binding sites of lectins were directed toward monosaccharides. They further concluded that α-*N*-acetylgalactosamine and α-L-fucose were the sugar determinants conferring A and H(O) blood group specificity, respectively. Both conclusions have been substantiated by subsequent investigations. The early work of Morgan and Watkins was, incidentally, among the first proofs for the presence of sugars on cell surfaces.

2.3 INTO THE LIMELIGHT

Notwithstanding these and other developments, lectins attracted only limited attention until the early 1960s. Two discoveries dramatically altered this attitude. The first was made in 1960 by Peter C. Nowell (Fig. 2.8) at the University of Pennsylvania, Philadelphia, who showed that the lectin of the red kidney bean (*Phaseolus vulgaris*), known as phytohaemagglutinin or PHA, is mitogenic; that is, it stimulates lymphocytes to undergo mitosis. This discovery had a revolutionary impact on immunology in that it shattered the view, held until then, that lymphocytes are dead-end cells that could neither divide nor differentiate further.

The chain of events that led to Nowell's discovery is worth recounting. It started in the late 1940s, when J.G. Li was working with the haematologist Edwin E. Osgood (at the University of Oregon Medical School in Portland) on the development of methods for long term culture of human leukaemic leukocytes

Fig. 2.8 Peter C. Nowell (b. 1928).

in vitro. Li conceived the idea that since beans contain embryos, they may possess growth promoting substances similar to those believed to be present in chicken embryo extracts and to be essential for the *in vitro* culture of mammalian cells. He therefore prepared a saline extract of red kidney beans and added it to blood samples enriched in lymphocytes. To his surprise he observed that while the erythrocytes were strongly agglutinated, the lymphocytes remained in suspension. Li and Osgood then went on to develop a method for the isolation of leukocytes from blood, based on the removal of the erythrocytes by their agglutination with extracts of red kidney beans. The method, the first to employ lectins for cell fractionation, became quite popular for a while. When Nowell started his studies of leukaemic cells in the late 1950s, he used PHA for the preparation of the lymphocytes for culture. He later recounted:

> My technician and I travelled across town one day to obtain some leukaemic blood, but found the patient was in remission. Rather than waste the trip, we cultured the (PHA treated) lymphocytes anyway and, to our surprise, found many mitoses. Culture of our own blood (similarly treated) promptly followed, confirming the suspicion that normal leukocytes were proliferating in our cultures.

The simplest explanation, that some factor in the tissue culture system caused this anomalous result, proved to be incorrect and eventually PHA was identified as the initiator of mitosis. Indeed, when other methods were used to separate red cells from leukocytes, no mitosis could be observed.

After Nowell submitted his manuscript to *Cancer Research*, one of the reviewers wrote that 'it is an interesting observation but of no conceivable significance to science'. Time did not take long to prove the reviewer wrong. Many biologists immediately took advantage of PHA to analyse the biochemical events that occur during lymphocyte stimulation *in vitro*. No less important was the fact that in the stimulated cells the chromosomes were easily visible, so that they could serve for facile chromosome analysis (karyotyping), sex determination and detection of chromosomal defects. As pointed out by the noted cytogeneticist T.C. Hsu in his book *Human and Mammalian Cytogenetics* [9], Nowell's discovery 'was one of the most timely and welcome contributions to human cytogenetics'.

A second mitogenic lectin was discovered a few years later, also as a result of an unusual series of events. In 1961, a 3-year-old girl was admitted to the Rhode Island Hospital at Providence with a mysterious fatal ailment. In the postmortem material taken from the child's brain, Drs Patricia Farnes and Barbara Barker observed cells that looked like large lymphocytes undergoing division (blast cells). Upon questioning the parents, the paediatricians found that the little girl had a habit of popping things into her mouth and swallowing the objects without chewing. There was a large pokeweed plant (*Phytolacca americana*) in her family's yard and apparently the girl had swallowed a considerable number of the berries. Pokeberries are unpalatable, so children usually chew one or two and stop. This particular child most likely swallowed quite a quantity, because when she first vomited, many berries and seeds were noted. Therefore, Farnes and Barker suspected that pokeweed contained a mitogen; this they indeed demonstrated by incubating extracts of the berries with lymphocytes.

Within a short time, several other lectins were proven to be mitogenic. Of special importance was the finding that concanavalin A acted as a mitogen since, in contrast to PHA, its activity could be inhibited by low concentrations of mannose. It was thus concluded that mitogenic stimulation is the result of binding of lectins to cell surface sugars. This was another early demonstration of the biological function of cell surface sugars.

It is also of interest that interleukin 2, a biologically active polypeptide originally known as T lymphocyte growth factor, was discovered in the growth medium of PHA stimulated lymphocytes in 1976 by Robert C. Gallo and his associates at the National Institutes of Health, Bathesda, MD. This was followed by the discovery of many other growth factors produced by activated lymphocytes and related cells, known as lymphokines or cytokines.

2.4 A TOOL FOR CANCER RESEARCH

Much excitement was generated in the biomedical community by the chance discovery that certain types of malignant cells are more readily agglutinated by lectins than are the corresponding normal cells. The discovery was reported in 1963 by Joseph C. Aub (Fig. 2.9) at the Massachusetts General Hospital in Boston, on the basis of research conducted after he had retired from the Harvard Medical School. Aub was one of the very few investigators who at that time believed that the difference between cancer cells and normal cells lay in their surface; in other words, that alterations in cell surface properties enable cancer cells to continue to multiply and to detach from their original site, spread through the body, lodge in a new environment and set up colonies there.

Such ideas seemed quite strange and most investigators considered them completely unfounded. To find out whether the surface of malignant cells was different from that of normal ones, Aub examined their response to incubation with several enzymes. Only in the case of one of the enzymes, a lipase from wheat germ, did he observe a difference: normal cells did not seem to be affected by the enzyme, but malignant cells were agglutinated. However, no agglutination occurred when he replaced the wheat germ lipase with a pancreatic lipase. Aub and his colleagues then found that the wheat germ lipase preparation contained, as a contaminant, a protein that was responsible for the agglutinating activity. This protein is now known as wheat germ agglutinin.

Aub's discovery began a new era in lectin research. It was immediately followed by the partial purification of wheat germ agglutinin by Max M. Burger of Princeton University, who conducted with it extensive studies of the surface changes that occur during the malignant transformation of cells. Wheat germ agglutinin was not available commercially, however, and it was not easy at the time to prepare it even

Fig. 2.9 Joseph C. Aub (1890–1973).

in partially purified form. It was only after Leo Sachs and Michael Inbar at the Weizmann Institute, Rehovot, Israel, found that the readily obtainable concanavalin A also agglutinated malignant cells preferentially that lectins became commonplace in many biological laboratories. Together with Sachs and Ben-Ami Sela, we found that soybean agglutinin also distinguished between normal and malignant cells, and other lectins have subsequently been shown to possess the same property.

2.5 REKINDLING OF INTEREST

The discovery of the mitogenic properties of lectins, and their ability to preferentially agglutinate malignant cells, rekindled interest in the properties of known lectins and led to an intense search for, and purification of, new ones. Of particular importance in the latter context was the introduction in 1965 – by Irwin J. Goldstein and B.B.L. Agrawal, at the University of Michigan – of affinity chromatography for the purification of lectins. Taking advantage of the fact that concanavalin A reacts with dextrans (polymers of α-linked glucose), they developed a simple and convenient technique for the direct isolation of the lectin from crude extracts of jack bean meal by specific adsorption on a column of commercially available crosslinked dextrans (Sephadex) and elution with glucose. This was another first for concanavalin A which, as mentioned, was also the first lectin to be purified by conventional techniques, the first to be crystallized and the first shown to be sugar specific. In the subsequent years, concanavalin A continued to lead the field of lectin research. Thus, it was the first lectin used for structural studies of carbohydrates, as well as for affinity purification of glycoproteins. In 1972, as a result of efforts by Gerald M. Edelman and his colleagues at the Rockefeller University, concanavalin A became the first lectin to be sequenced. At the same time, Edelman's group, and independently Karl Hardman and Clinton F. Ainsworth at IBM Laboratories, established the three dimensional structure of this lectin. In 1983, concanavalin A became the first lectin in space, where it served as a mitogen in a study of the effect of weightlessness on cell proliferation [10].

2.6 INSIGHT INTO BIOLOGICAL FUNCTIONS

Two key observations have provided insight into the function of lectins in nature. The first had its origin in the discovery in 1941 – by George K. Hirst in New York and Ronald Hare in Toronto – that the influenza virus agglutinated erythrocytes. The molecular basis for this haemagglutination phenomenon was obscure for more than a decade. Mainly through the efforts of Alfred Gottschalk in Australia, it was shown, in the early 1950s, that the virus binds to erythrocytes and other cells through *N*-acetylneuraminic acid residues present on their surface and that this binding is a prerequisite for initiation of infection. The viral haemagglutinin responsible for the binding has subsequently been purified, crystallized and studied in detail. Although the above studies unequivocally demonstrated that a lectin was involved in a recognition process, their significance as a clue to the understanding of the biological function of lectins was overlooked for a long time.

The second clue came with the discovery in 1974 – by Gilbert Ashwell at the National Institute of Health, Bethesda and Anatol G. Morell at the Albert Einstein College, New York – of the first mammalian lectin, the hepatic binding protein specific for galactose, and the demonstration that it may be involved in the clearance of glycoproteins from the circulatory system. These important findings, too, originated from an unexpected observation. During studies initiated in the late 1960s on the biological role of ceruloplasmin, a copper transport glycoprotein present in serum, Ashwell and Morell observed that when ceruloplasmin from which *N*-acetylneuraminic acid had been removed by treatment with sialidase was injected into rabbits, it disappeared from circulation within minutes, in striking contrast to native ceruloplasmin which remained in circulation for many hours. Experiments with other serum glycoproteins, such as fetuin, have also shown that desialylation, which results in unmasking of terminal galactose residues on the glycoproteins, leads to a remarkable shortening of the survival of the glycoproteins in circulation. It was also found that soon after their disappearence from the serum, the intact asialoglycoproteins accumulated in the liver. Indeed, liver membranes were shown to specifically bind desialylated glycoproteins, as well as glycopeptides and oligosaccharides with terminal galactose residues. The glycoprotein involved in this binding was purified and shown to behave as a typical lectin, specific for galactose and its derivatives, including galactose terminated glycoproteins.

2.7 INTO CONTEMPORARY LECTIN RESEARCH

These studies bring us out of history into the contemporary period of lectin research. It is characterized by a rapid accumulation of knowledge about the occurrence, chemical properties and biological activities of lectins, an ever-growing interest in their applications in biology and medicine and a continuous quest for the elucidation of their function(s) in nature, subjects to be discussed in the following chapters of this book.

CHAPTER 3
Occurrence and isolation

The simplest way to detect the presence of a lectin in a biological material is to prepare a water or buffer extract from this material and to examine its ability to agglutinate erythrocytes or to precipitate a polysaccharide or glycoprotein. If a positive result is obtained, it is essential to show that agglutination or precipitation is specifically inhibited by mono- or oligosaccharides, i.e. it is sugar specific (Fig. 3.1).

Haemagglutination is usually determined by the serial dilution technique using erythrocytes from humans or rabbits. Occasionally erythrocytes that have been treated with trypsin or sialidase are employed, since such cells are often more

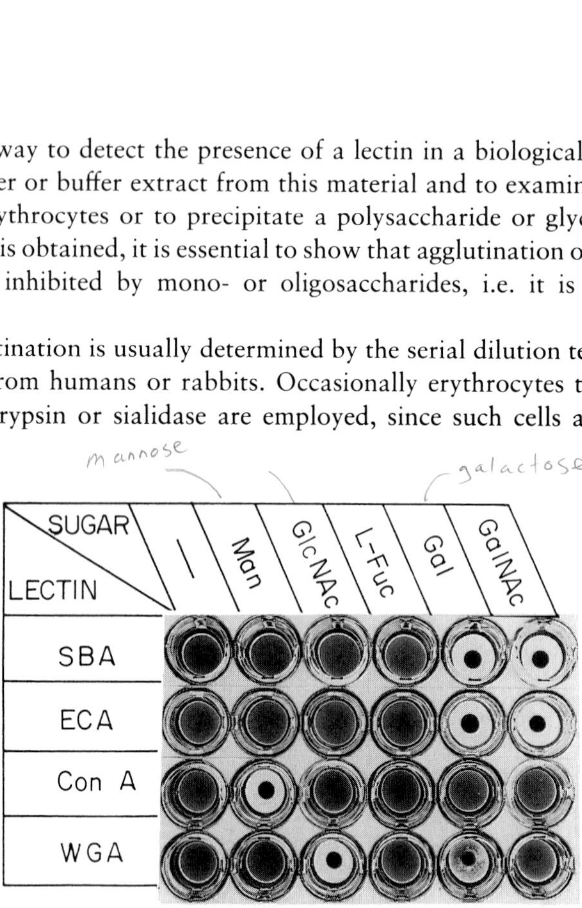
SUGAR
LECTIN
—
Man
GlcNAc
L-Fuc
Gal
GalNAc
SBA
ECA
Con A
WGA

Fig. 3.1 Determination of carbohydrate specificities of lectins by inhibition of haemagglutination. Ground seeds (or wheat germ) were extracted with ten times their weight of phosphate buffered saline. In the case of soybeans, the oil was removed prior to extraction. Each well of the microtitre plate contained 0.05 ml extract, 0.05 ml 4% suspension of rabbit erythrocytes and 0.05 ml 0.2 M sugar solution. The agglutinated erythrocytes form a carpet that covers the whole well; where no agglutination occurred, the cells form a button at the bottom of the well. Picture taken after 2 h at room temperature. SBA, soybean agglutinin; ECA, *Erythrina cristagalli* agglutinin; Con A, concanavalin A; WGA, wheat germ agglutinin.

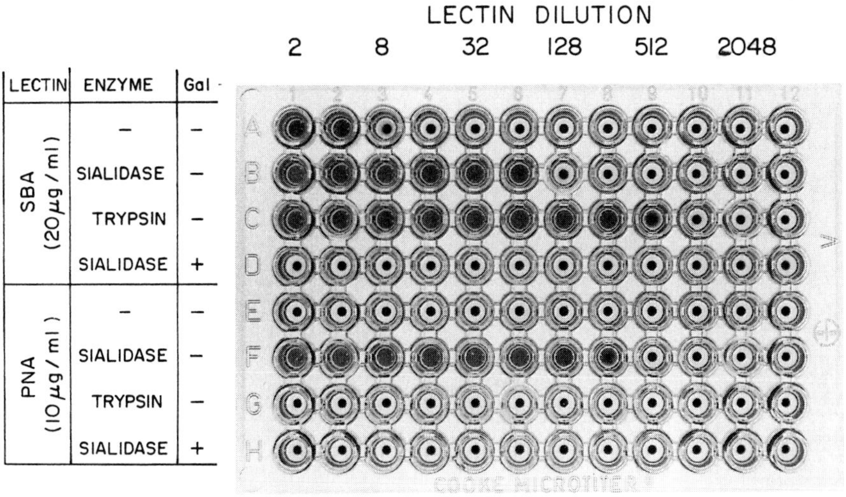
LECTIN DILUTION
2 8 32 128 512 2048
LECTIN
ENZYME
Gal
SBA (20 µg / ml)
–
SIALIDASE
TRYPSIN
SIALIDASE
PNA (10 µg / ml)
–
SIALIDASE
TRYPSIN
SIALIDASE
–
–
–
+
–
–
–
+
COOKE MICROTITER

Fig. 3.2 Effect of enzyme treatment of human erythrocytes on their agglutination by soybean agglutinin (SBA) and peanut agglutinin (PNA) without or with galactose (Gal).

sensitive to agglutination than untreated cells (Fig. 3.2). The same methods are also used to monitor the activity of lectins during purification.

3.1 OCCURRENCE

Lectins occur in all classes and families of organisms, although not necessarily in every genus or species [1–3].

3.1.1 Plants

Lectins have been detected in more than 1000 species of plants. The richest sources are mature seeds, especially those of the legumes, where lectins may constitute as much as 10% of the total protein of the seed. The distribution of lectins within the seeds differs among various plant families. In seeds of the legumes, most of the lectin is localized in the cotyledons, in organelles known as protein bodies. In seeds of Euphorbiacea (e.g. *Ricinus communis*), the major location of the lectins is in the endosperm and here, too, they are confined mainly to the protein bodies. In cereals, all of the lectin is found in the seed embryo. Besides seeds, lectins are found in tubers (e.g. potato) and fruits (e.g. tomato and cucumber), although at much lower levels than in legume seeds (Table 3.1). Small amounts of lectins are present in other plant tissues, such as leaves, bark and roots.

Most plant tissues contain a single lectin, but examples are known of seeds that contain two (or more) lectins that differ in their sugar specificities and other

Table 3.1 Non-seed plant lectins

Tissue	*Plant*
Bark	*Robinia pseudoacacia*
	Elderberry
Bulb	Snow drop
Fruit	Tomato
Fruiting bodies	Common mushroom
Leaves	*Dolichos biflorus*
	Griffonia simplicifolia
	Sophora japonica
Roots	Pokeweed
Tuber	Potato

properties. Thus, two lectins are found in the seeds of gorse (*Ulex europaeus*), one specific for *N*-acetylglucosamine and the other for L-fucose. Two lectins with distinct sugar specificities, one specific for *N*-acetylgalactosamine and the other specific for mannose, are found in the seeds of *Vicia cracca*. Several lectins are present in the seeds of *Griffonia simplicifolia*, specific for *N*-acetylgalactosamine, galactose or *N*-acetylglucosamine. Castor beans contain two closely related lectins, the cytotoxic ricin and the relatively non-toxic *Ricinus communis* agglutinin. Similarly, the seeds of *Abrus precatorius* contain a toxic lectin, abrin, and an agglutinin of low toxicity.

3.1.2 Vertebrates

In vertebrates, two classes of lectin have been distinguished with respect to their localization – soluble lectins and membrane bound ones; the latter require detergents for their solubilization. Although the soluble lectins from the serum of the eels *Anguilla anguilla* and *Anguilla rostrata* have been known for 50 years and were purified several decades ago, lectins in aqueous extracts of vertebrate tissues were found only relatively recently. The first of these were obtained in the 1970s from the electric organ of the electric eel, *Electrophorus electricus*, and from calf heart and lung. A variety of lectins, some of which are similar to these just mentioned and others that differ in their sugar specificity and molecular structure, have subsequently been discovered in various other tissues of mammals, birds, amphibia and reptiles [10a].

Membrane lectins have been found in the liver of various animals, such as rabbit, rat and chicken, both in hepatocytes and in Kupffer cells. They are associated both with the plasma membrane and with intracellular membranes.

3.1.3 Invertebrates

Lectins have been detected in practically all classes and subclasses of invertebrates examined, such as crabs, snails, worms and molluscs. They are present mainly in the haemolymph and sexual organs, e.g. albumin glands and eggs, and occur also on the membranes of haemocytes, cells that function as unspecific immunological protectors.

Perhaps the best known invertebrate lectin is that from the garden snail, *Helix pomatia*; it is specific for human blood type A determinants and is inhibited by α-linked *N*-acetylgalactosamine. Many invertebrate lectins, however, are specific for sialic acids, usually for *N*-acetylneuraminic acid (e.g. the lectin from horseshoe crab, *Limulus polyphemus*, first reported by H. Noguchi in 1903).

3.1.4 Microorganisms

Most enterobacteria (e.g. *Escherichia coli* and *Salmonellae* spp.) possess the ability to produce surface lectins in the form of submicroscopic hair-like appendages known as fimbriae (pili) (Fig. 3.3). Surface lectins are also produced by other bacteria, such as various species of Actinomyces. In a few cases, e.g. *Pseudomonas aeruginosa*, the lectins are intracellular and not present on the cell surface.

Lectins occur in protozoa as well. The pathogenic amoeba, *Entamoeba*

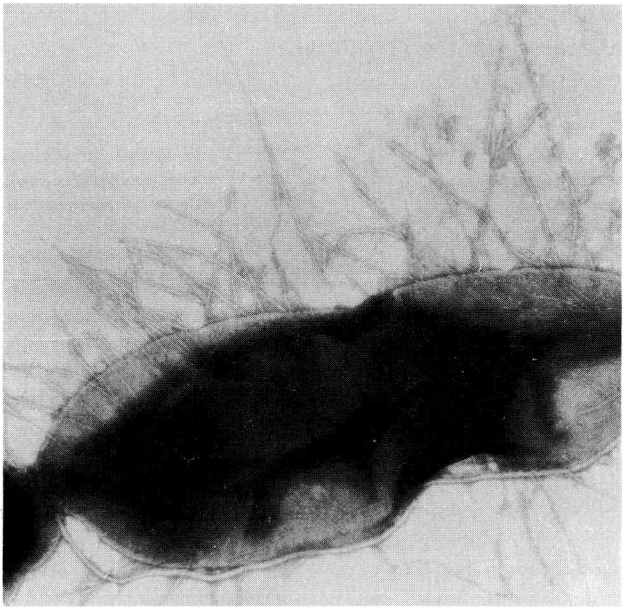

Fig. 3.3 Type I fimbriated *Escherichia coli* (Courtesy of Abner M. Mhashilkar.)

histolytica, produces two distinct lectins, one specific for oligomers of *N*-acetylglucosamine and the other for galactose and *N*-acetylgalactosamine [11, 12]. An unusual type of lectin has been found in *Giardia lamblia*, a widely distributed protozoan flagellate that causes diarrhoea in man; inactive in its native form, it is activated by mild proteolysis [13].

3.1.5 Viruses

Viruses contain surface proteins or glycoproteins which serve for their attachment to host cells. Several of these bind sugars, primarily *N*-acetylneuraminic acid, and act as haemagglutinins. They can, therefore, be considered as lectins. The best characterized of these lectins are those of the influenza virus and of Sendai virus, belonging to the myxoviruses and paramyxoviruses, respectively [14].

3.2 ISOLATION

Purification of lectins is essential in order to establish their molecular properties and is highly desirable for their numerous applications. In the past, lectins were isolated by traditional methods of protein fractionation such as salt precipitation or ion exchange chromatography. Currently, affinity chromatography, which is based on the ability of lectins to bind sugars reversibly, is the method of choice. Knowledge of the sugar specificity of a lectin, which can be obtained using a crude lectin preparation, for example a seed extract, permits the design of a suitable

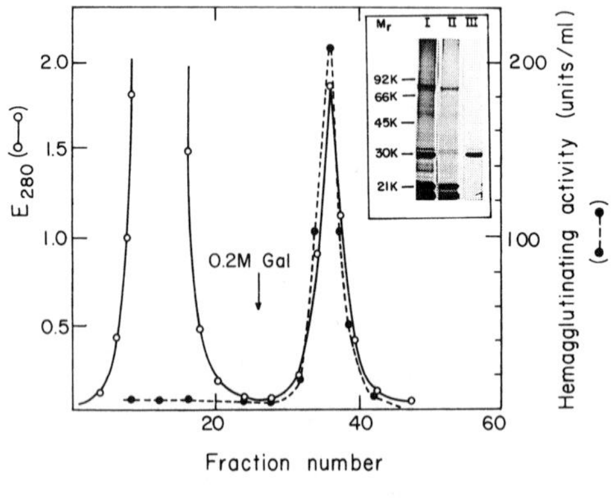

E_{280} (o—o)
2.0
1.5
1.0
0.5
0.2M Gal
20
40
60
Fraction number
200
100
Hemagglutinating activity (units/ml) (●--●)
Mr
I II III
92K
66K
45K
30K
21K

Fig. 3.4 Isolation of *Erythrina cristagalli* lectin from a crude seed protein preparation by affinity chromatography on a column of galactose-derivatized Sepharose 4B. The first peak is inactive protein eluted with phosphate buffered saline, and the second peak is the pure lectin eluted with galactose: (○——○), protein; (●——●), haemagglutinating activity. Inset: analysis by polyacrylamide gel electrophoresis of: I, crude protein preparation applied to column; II, first peak; III, second peak. M – molecular weight markers.

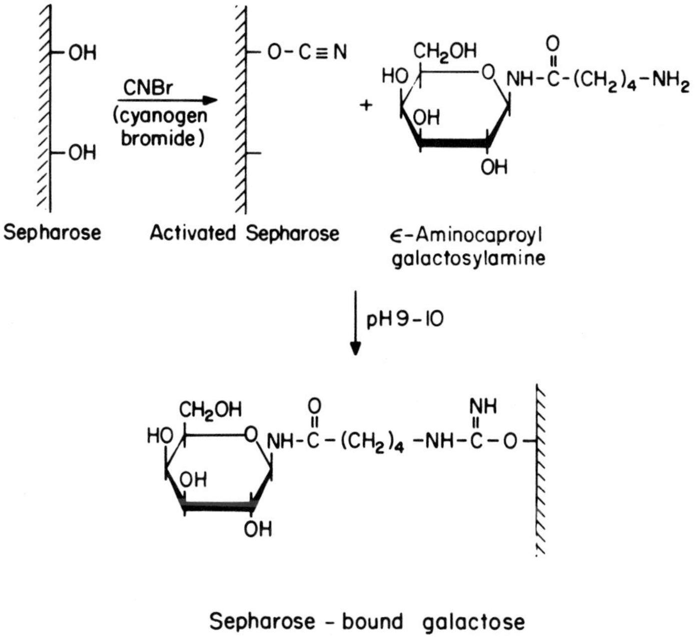

-OH
-OH
CNBr
(cyanogen bromide)
-O-C≡N
+
CH₂OH
HO
O
NH-C-(CH₂)₄-NH₂
OH
OH
Sepharose
Activated Sepharose
ε-Aminocaproyl galactosylamine
pH 9-10
NH
NH-C-(CH₂)₄-NH-C-O
Sepharose - bound galactose

Fig. 3.5 Schematic representation of the synthesis of a galactose containing affinity chromatography column.

affinity chromatography procedure. The crude, or partially purified, preparation is passed through the affinity column, the unadsorbed material is washed off and the lectin is eluted with a solution of an inhibitory sugar (Fig. 3.4). The affinity purified preparation thus obtained is frequently homogenous when examined by a variety of criteria and does not require further purification.

A wide range of affinity adsorbents, to suit any taste or purse, have been described in the literature [15] and many of them can be purchased ready-made. These include polysaccharides such as Sephadex, a polymer of glucose employed for the purification of concanavalin A and pea lectin; agarose (or Sepharose), a polymer of galactose, used for the purification of the lectin from castor bean; and chitin, a polymer of *N*-acetylglucosamine, used for the purification of wheat germ agglutinin. In the absence of readily available polysaccharides, columns consisting of carbohydrates covalently attached to an insoluble carrier are employed. The carbohydrate can be linked to the carrier as such, in the form of a suitable synthetic derivative, or as part of a glycoprotein or glycopeptide (Fig. 3.5). For instance, lactose coupled to Sepharose is the reagent of choice for the purification of the lectins from peanuts, eel electric organ or calf heart muscle. *N*-acetylglucosamine bound to the same support is frequently used for the purification of the lectin from potato, and immobilized porcine A + H blood type substance is used for the purification of the blood type A specific lectins from *Dolichos biflorus* and *Helix pomatia*.

CHAPTER 4
Biological activities

All cells come in a sugar coating, which consists of carbohydrate chains of membrane glycoproteins and glycolipids (in eukaryotes) or of polysaccharides (in prokaryotes). These carbohydrates serve as potential sites of attachment for lectins. Such attachment may induce a variety of changes in the cell, which are an expression of the biological activities of lectins. Studies of these activities, and a search for other, still unknown ones, are of interest for several reasons. They are useful for the detection and assay of lectins; they serve as a basis for the manifold applications of lectins and for the development of new ones; they provide us with a means to investigate different cellular and subcellular processes, especially those initiated at the cell surface; and last, but not least, the biological activities of lectins detected in the laboratory give clues to the probable functions of these substances in nature.

4.1 CELL AGGLUTINATION

Agglutination is the most easily detectable manifestation of the interaction of a lectin with cells and has been used since the early days of lectin research to reveal the presence of a lectin in a biological material. It is the outcome of the formation of cross-links between cells in suspension. Binding of a lectin to the cells is a necessary, albeit not sufficient, condition for agglutination to occur. The reason for this is that agglutination, although seemingly simple, is a complex process which is affected by many factors, such as the molecular properties of the lectin (e.g. molecular size and number of saccharide binding sites), cell surface properties (e.g. number and accessibility of lectin binding sites, membrane fluidity), and metabolic state of the cells. The relative contributions of the different factors depends upon both the lectin and the cells used. In addition, agglutination is affected by external conditions such as temperature, cell concentration, mixing and so on. When agglutination does occur and is inhibited by an appropriate sugar, it serves as an indication that carbohydrate structures for which the lectin is specific are present on the surface of the cells. Agglutination by lectins can thus be used to obtain information on the nature of carbohydrates present on cells and to follow changes of cell surfaces during normal and pathological processes such as growth, development or

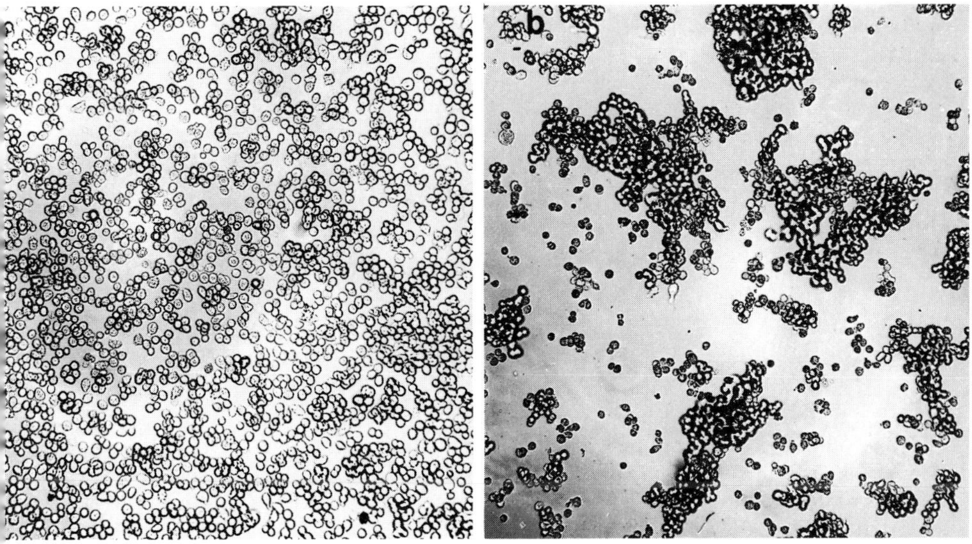
b

Fig. 4.1 Normal rat cells (left) and cells that have been transformed by a cancer inducing virus (right) after incubation for 30 min with 100 μg soybean agglutinin per ml. (Reproduced with permission from Sela, B., Lis, H., Sharon, N. and Sachs, L. (1970) *J. Membrane Biol.*, 3, 267–79.)

malignant transformation (Fig. 4.1). No less important is the fact that selective agglutination of a particular cell population in a heterogenous cell preparation provides a simple and efficient means for its fractionation into biologically distinct subpopulations (sections 9.4 and 9.6.3).

Cells that are not agglutinated by low concentrations of a lectin often become agglutinable after mild proteolysis (Fig.3.2). Trypsin or papain treated erythrocytes are therefore frequently used along with untreated cells when searching for new lectins, or as indicator cells in routine lectin assays. Enzymes that modify carbohydrates on cell surfaces may also have remarkable effects on the agglutination of cells by lectins. Thus, human erythrocytes are not agglutinated by peanut agglutinin even at concentrations as high as 1 mg lectin/ml. In contrast, sialidase treated erythrocytes are agglutinated by as little as 0.04 μg/ml of lectin (Fig. 3.2). This is because removal of *N*-acetylneuraminic acid results in exposure of galactose residues for which peanut agglutinin is specific.

4.2 MITOGENIC STIMULATION OF LYMPHOCYTES

4.2.1 General features

One of the most dramatic effects of the interaction of lectins with cells is observed with lymphocytes. Incubation of lymphocytes with very low concentrations of

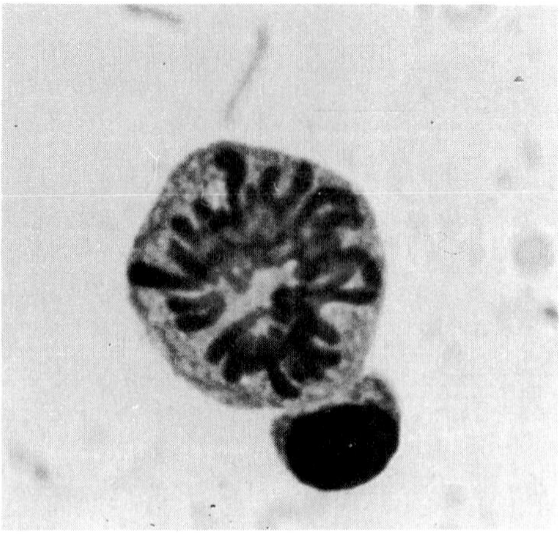

Fig. 4.2 Photomicrograph of two lymphocytes after incubation for 3 days with concanavalin A. One of the cells has entered the metaphase stage of mitosis, in which it is enlarged and its chromosomes are visible as discrete structures. (Courtesy of Abraham Novogrodsky.)

certain lectins (about 1–5 μg/ml) induces them to grow and divide. The triggering of quiescent, non-dividing lymphocytes into a state of growth and proliferation (Fig. 4.2) known as 'mitogenic stimulation' is a phenomenon of cardinal importance since it is a key event in the immune response of the body against foreign agents (antigens). Mitogenic stimulation is routinely monitored by measuring the increase in the rate of incorporation of labelled thymidine into DNA after incubation of the lymphocytes for 48–72 h with varying concentrations of the mitogen tested (Fig. 4.3).

Subsequent to the discovery in the 1960s of the mitogenic activity of PHA,

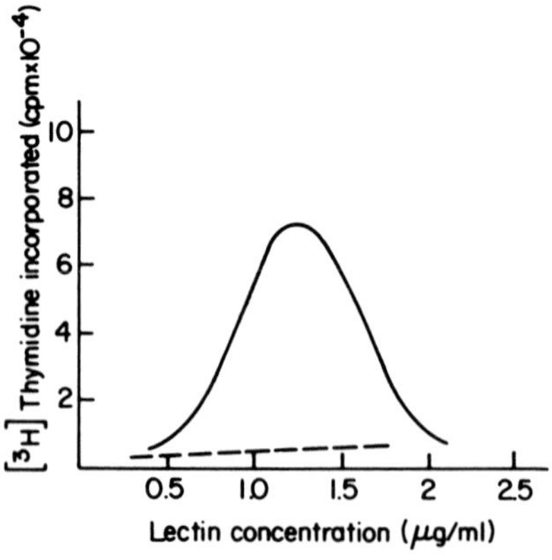
[3H] Thymidine incorporated (cpm×10-4)
10
8
6
4
2
0.5
1.0
1.5
2
2.5
Lectin concentration (μg/ml)

Fig. 4.3 Typical dose response curve of mitogenic stimulation of human peripheral blood lymphocytes by concanavalin A. Stimulation determined by measuring the incorporation of [^{3}H]thymidine into DNA after 48 h incubation of the cells with the lectin in the absence (solid line) or presence (broken line) of methyl α-mannoside.

pokeweed mitogen and concanavalin A (section 2.3), many other lectins were found to possess similar activity (Table 4.1). The majority of these are from plants, and a few are from animals, slime molds or bacteria. Most mitogenic lectins stimulate only the thymus dependent population of lymphocytes (T cells or T lymphocytes) and are inactive for mitosis of the other class of lymphocytes, the thymus independent (or B) cells. Exceptions are the lectins from the crab *Homarus americanus* and from the slime mold *Dictyostelium purpureum* that stimulate B cells but not T cells and pokeweed mitogen that stimulates both T and B cells.

An important property of mitogenic lectins is their ability to stimulate a large proportion (sometimes as much as 70–80%) of the susceptible lymphocytes, irrespective of the antigenic specificity of the cells. Antigens, in contrast, stimulate only specific clones, each of which comprises a tiny proportion, 0.1% or less, of the total number of lymphocytes. Because of their ability to stimulate multiple lymphocyte clones, lectins are classified as polyclonal mitogens. Such amplification of the mitogenic response by lectins greatly facilitates the detection and study of the changes associated with cell proliferation.

Essentially all metabolic processes examined in mitogen treated lymphocytes are stimulated, though to varying degrees and at different times after exposure to the

Table 4.1 Mitogenic lectins

	Cell specificity	
Lectin	*T*	*B*
Plant		
Concanavalin A	+	
Erythrina cristagalli	+	
Lentil	+	
Pea	+	
PHA	+	
Pokeweed	+	+
Wistaria floribunda	+	
Animal		
Beetle	+	
Lobster		+
Rabbit liver*	+	
Microorganism		
Pseudomonas aeruginosa	+	
Slime mold		+

*Active only on sialidase treated cells.

mitogen. Many of these changes occur immediately after the addition of the mitogen, some of them within seconds to minutes. The earliest detectable changes are in the membrane. These include increased permeability for metabolites, e.g. glucose and amino acids, and an accelerated turnover of membrane phospholipids. Among the early intracellular events are stimulation of acetylation of histones, phosphorylation of nuclear proteins and modification of lipid and protein metabolism. Some 10–20 h later, RNA and protein synthesis accelerate and morphological changes become apparent. At about 48 h, DNA synthesis starts and later the cells enter mitosis. This is followed by the reversion of the post-mitotic cells to small lymphocytes resembling those originally stimulated or, if the mitogen remains in the medium, restimulation of some of the cells to undergo another cycle of proliferation.

In addition to these events, which are common to most cells undergoing active growth, stimulated lymphocytes exhibit certain unique features. Soon after activation, they release a variety of lymphokines, the best characterized of which are γ-interferon and interleukin 2(IL-2). At about 72–96 h after stimulation, other differentiated functions of activated lymphocytes are detected, such as immunoglobulin production by B cells and the appearance of effector cells with well defined immunological activities. The latter include helper and suppressor cells that participate in the regulation of the immune response.

4.2.2 Mechanism of stimulation

It is widely presumed that mitogenic stimulation by lectins involves a two step signalling mechanism. The initial step is binding of the lectin to cell surface sugars: if the lectin is removed by washing with a solution of the specific sugar, no stimulation occurs. Binding alone, however, is not sufficient since certain lectins (e.g. those from *Helix pomatia* and the Japanese pagoda tree *Sophora japonica*), do not stimulate human lymphocytes even though they bind well to these cells. It has been suggested that mitogenic lectins interact with unique membrane components that may act as 'triggering receptors' and that non-mitogenic lectins may not recognize these components. Recent work with human lymphocytes and lymphocyte cell lines has indicated that for stimulation to occur, the lectin must bind to the T cell antigen receptor [16, 17], which is the surface component involved in antigen specific stimulation. The nature of the mitogen induced signals that traverse the cell membrane to initiate the intracellular processes which culminate in DNA synthesis is not known. A signal transduction pathway that was recently shown to function in antigen dependent activation of lymphocytes [18, 19] appears to be set in motion also in lectin mediated stimulation. The key event in this pathway is the enzymatic hydrolysis of phosphatidylinositol 4, 5-bisphosphate into diacylglycerol and inositol 1, 4, 5-trisphosphate that act as second messengers (Fig. 4.4). The inositol 1, 4, 5-trisphosphate is released into the cytoplasm where it mobilizes Ca^{2+} from a mitochondrial pool. Diacylglycerol is the putative

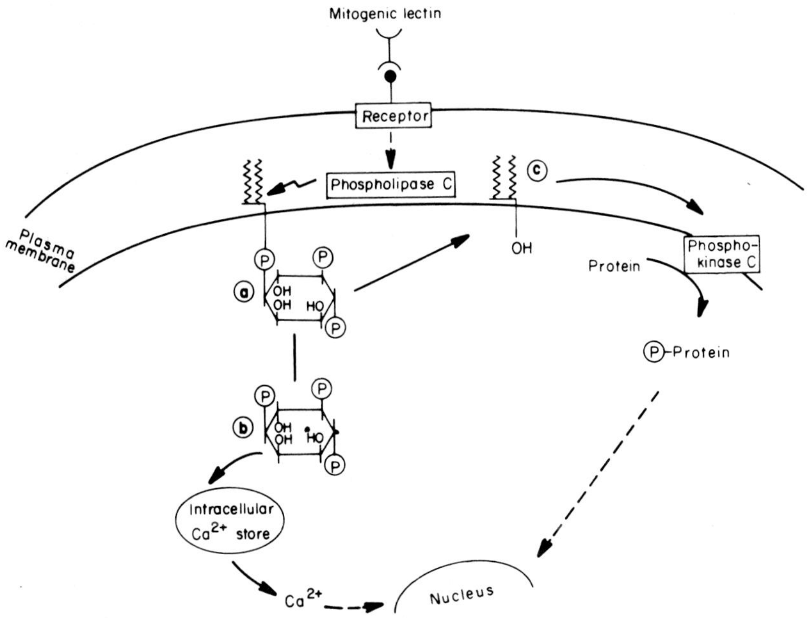
Mitogenic lectin
Receptor
Phospholipase C
Plasma membrane
Phospho-
kinase C
Protein
OH
P-Protein
Intracellular
Ca2+ store
Ca2+
Nucleus

Fig. 4.4 Model of transmembrane signal transduction in mitogenic stimulation. Interaction between the mitogen and its receptor activates the enzyme phospholipase C, which hydrolyses phosphatidylinositol 4,5-bisphosphate (compound a) into inositol 1,4,5-trisphosphate (compound b) and diacylglycerol (compound c). The last two compounds act synergistically as secondary messengers to elicit physiological responses.

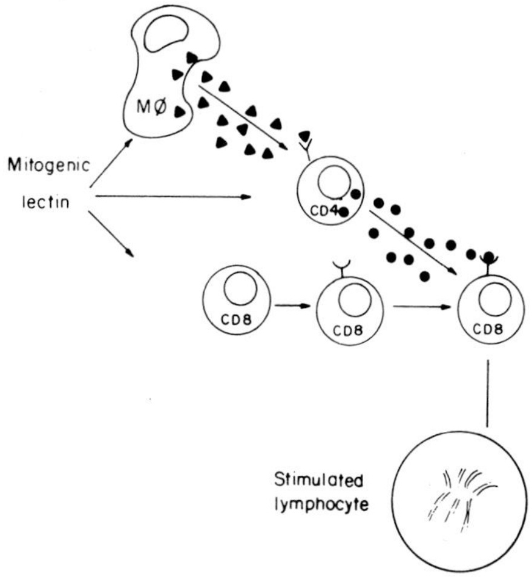
MØ
Mitogenic
lectin
CD4
CD8
CD8
CD8
Stimulated
lymphocyte

Fig.4.5 Model of cell cooperation in the mitogenic stimulation of T lymphocytes; Mϕ, macrophage; ▲ interleukin 1; ●, interleukin 2; CD4, helper lymphocyte; CD8, suppressor lymphocyte.

physiological activator of protein kinase C, a key enzyme involved in many cell activation reactions (e.g. by hormones). The concerted action of the two messengers, diacylglycerol and inositol 1, 4, 5-trisphosphate, triggers processes that result in the production and release of interleukin 2 by one set of lymphocytes and the induction of functional receptors for this lymphokine in another (Fig. 4.5). Production of interleukin 2 requires the participation of accessory cells (macrophages) that provide a soluble factor – interleukin 1 (IL-1). Once interleukin 2 and its receptors become available, the stage is set for the second step of lymphocyte activation: the lymphokine binds to its receptors which leads, in an as yet unknown way, to DNA synthesis and cell division.

4.3 LECTIN MEDIATED KILLING OF ANIMAL TARGET CELLS

Certain subpopulations of lymphocytes, known as cytotoxic T cells, and under some circumstances macrophages, can lyse target cells to which they are closely bound. The range of target cells is usually limited since binding requires the specific recognition by killer cells of the major histocompatibility complex antigens of the target cells. In contrast, in the presence of concanavalin A or other mitogenic lectins, a wide variety of antigenically unrelated target cells are lysed by cytotoxic T lymphocytes, a phenomenon known as lectin dependent cytotoxicity. The lack of immune specificity in the lectin dependent reaction has been attributed to the ability of the lectin to bind to both effector and target cells, thus promoting the proximity necessary to facilitate the cytolytic activity of the effector cell. Bridging, however, is not sufficient to bring about the death of the target cells, since non-mitogenic lectins also bind to the cells but do not cause lysis. It has therefore been proposed that the lectin itself plays no direct role in the intercellular recognition or in the activation process, but acts by binding to, and modifying, the surface of the target cells (including structures that are products of the major histocompatibility gene complex), rendering them recognizable by the cytotoxic T lymphocytes. The mechanism by which cytotoxic lymphocytes recognize and lyse target cells in lectin dependent cytotoxicity would thus be analogous to that operating in killing mediated by specific cytotoxic T lymphocytes.

Another form of lectin dependent cytotoxicity is the killing of tumour cells by macrophages. It is mediated by a limited number of plant lectins (e.g., of wheat germ and *Griffonia simplicifolia*) and the lectin of the flesh-fly, *Sarcophaga peregrina*, that bind to carbohydrates on both the killer and target cells. This activity is analogous to that of anti-tumour antibodies that induce macrophages to lyse tumours. Lectin dependent cytotoxicity and antigen dependent cytotoxicity of macrophages exhibit certain similarities, for instance in the requirement of contact between the cells and in the time course of the reaction. They differ, however, in their target specificity, in that antigen dependent cytotoxicity is restricted to cells carrying the appropriate antigen whereas the lectin mediated reaction is not. Lectin mediated cytotoxicity may occur *in vivo* since interperitoneal injection of *Griffonia simplicifolia* lectin I protected mice inoculated with Ehrlich ascites tumour cells from tumour growth and subsequent death.

4.4 PHAGOCYTOSIS OF YEASTS AND BACTERIA

In addition to lectin dependent killing of tumour cells by macrophages, lectins mediate binding and phagocytosis of other types of cell. Yeast cells (*Saccharomyces cerevisiae*) pre-coated with concanavalin A bind in large numbers to, and are phagocytosed by, mouse peritoneal macrophages. Wheat germ agglutinin also markedly enhances the binding and phagocytosis by mouse peritoneal macrophages of bacteria such as *Staphylococcus aureus* H, *Staphylococcus albus* or *Micrococcus luteus*.

4.5 INSULIN-LIKE ACTIVITY

Concanavalin A, wheat germ agglutinin and several other lectins mimic the effects of insulin on adipocytes, such as stimulation of lipogenesis and of glucose transport and inhibition of lipolysis. Moreover, concanavalin A also stimulates, like insulin, synthesis of glycogen by diaphragm muscle and accumulation of lipids in adipose tissue *in vivo*. Lectins probably exert their insulinomimetic action by binding to the carbohydrate moiety of the insulin receptor which, like many other receptors on the cell surface, is a glycoprotein. The foregoing assumption is supported by the finding that concanavalin A and wheat germ agglutinin mimic the ability of insulin to stimulate the phosphokinase activity of purified insulin receptor, a reaction believed to be a major step in the mechanism of action of the hormone.

4.6 CYTOTOXICITY

Several lectins, e.g. concanavalin A, wheat germ agglutinin and the lectin from *Robinia pseudoacacia*, are toxic to mammalian cells in culture and to animals. Their toxicity is, however, at least 1000 times lower than that of ricin and abrin. Indeed, ricin is one of the deadliest poisons known; it is by weight about ten times as poisonous as cobra venom. In 1978, it came to the attention of the general public after it was used as a weapon in the notorius, politically motivated 'umbrella murder'. In September of that year, while crossing London's Waterloo Bridge, Georgi Markov, Bulgarian writer and broadcaster in exile, was jostled by an unknown man with an umbrella. Three days later Markov was dead. Upon autopsy a hollow platinum pellet, the size of a pinhead, with a tiny hole of less than $\frac{1}{3}$mm^3, was removed from his body. The dimensions of the hole, together with the symptoms observed, led to the conclusion that ricin was the killing agent, since very few poisons are sufficiently potent to kill a man at such a minute amount.

Ricin (as well as the related plant toxins abrin, modeccin, volkensin and viscumin) is a heterodimer composed of two polypeptide chains, A and B, linked via a single disulphide bond (section 6.1). The heavier (B) chain possesses the carbohydrate binding sites (specific for galactose and *N*-acetylgalactosamine), whereas the lighter (A) chain is devoid of such sites. The A chain inhibits protein synthesis in cell-free systems, thus representing the toxic moiety of the molecule. However, for toxic action on cells, the intact molecule is required. Subsequent to binding to the cell surface via the B chain, the toxin is taken up by the cell where the A chain inhibits protein synthesis by interfering with peptide chain elongation on polyribosomes. The mechanism of cell toxicity of the A chains of ricin and abrin at the molecular level has only very recently been clarified [20–22]. The toxins cleave an *N*-glycosidic bond that links adenine to ribose at a single position (A4324) of one of the ribosomal RNA species (28S RNA). The removal of the adenine inactivates the ribosome, and thus the whole machinery of protein synthesis. Acting as an enzyme, each toxin molecule therefore inactivates numerous ribosomes, which explains why these substances are so toxic: it has been calculated that a single molecule is sufficient to kill a cell. Interestingly, A4324 lies in a region of 28S ribosomal RNA that is highly conserved between animal species, as well as some other organisms. This may account for the toxicity of ricin to a wide range of organisms.

Attempts are being made to take advantage of the high toxicity of ricin for therapeutic purposes, through the construction of immunotoxins. These are hybrid molecules, made by covalently linking a toxin (usually ricin) to monoclonal antibodies against the cells that one wishes to kill. The antibodies guide the immunotoxin to the target cells, which are then eliminated by the action of the toxin [23, 24] (section 9.6.3).

4.7 NUTRITIONAL ASPECTS

As mentioned in the previous section, a few lectins are highly toxic to animals and several others possess low toxicity. The fact that lectins are widely distributed in common food items and animal feeds raises, therefore, the important question whether they pose any significant risk to the health of humans or farm animals [25, 26]. This is particularly relevant in relation to foods such as vegetables and fruits that are consumed raw or lightly cooked. Even with food items that are eaten in cooked form, the cooking may not always be adequate to completely inactivate the lectins present. That this is a real risk is evidenced by several outbreaks of food poisoning that have been caused by eating insufficiently cooked beans. As a preventive measure, a warning label is now attached to cans and packets of dry red kidney beans sold in retail markets in England (Fig. 4.6).

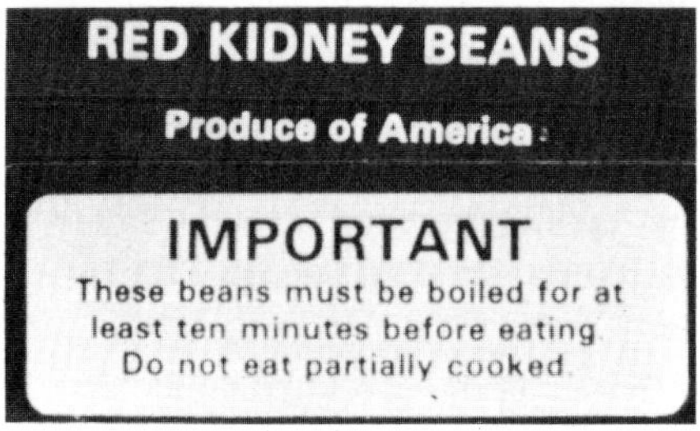
RED KIDNEY BEANS
Produce of America
IMPORTANT
These beans must be boiled for at least ten minutes before eating.
Do not eat partially cooked.

Fig. 4.6 Warning label on packets of dry red kidney beans.

It should also be noted that several lectins are resistant to proteolysis in the gastrointestinal tract. For example, following ingestion of tomato lectin and wheat germ agglutinin by volunteers, much of the lectin was recovered intact in stools. While in the intestine, the lectins may bind to carbohydrates on cells of the mucosa, and thus interfere with the digestive, protective or secretory functions of this organ. For instance, kidney bean lectins ingested by rats in the form of raw beans bind to the lumenal surface of microvilli in the duodenum and jejunum, resulting in the appearance of lesions and severe disruption and abnormal development of the microvilli (Fig. 4.7). A major consequence associated with the intake of lectins is a serious impairment of the absorption of nutrients such as sugars, lipids and amino acids across the intestinal wall, possibly due to changes in intestinal permeability [27]. Lectins could also interfere with the normal process of food absorption by interacting with brush border hydrolases which play a role in

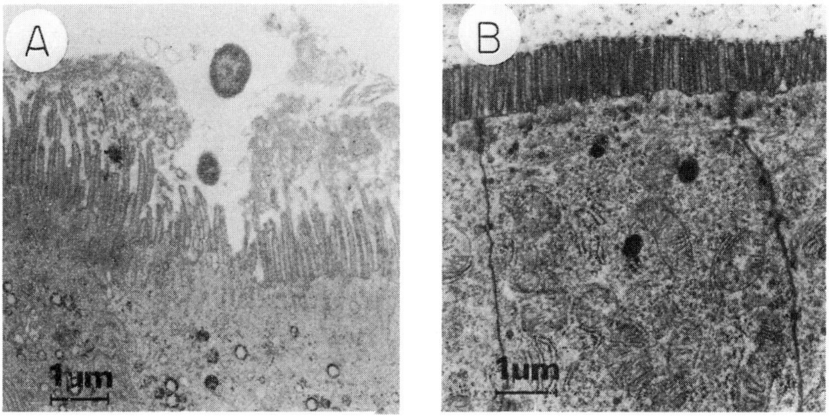
A
1μm
B
1μm

Fig. 4.7 Electron micrographs of sections through the apical regions of duodenal enterocytes from rats fed diets containing 5% raw kidney beans and 5% casein, showing severely disrupted microvilli (A), compared with 10% casein, showing normal microvilli (B). (From Pusztai, A., Clarke, E.M.W., King, T.P. and Stewart, J.C. (1979) *J. Sci. Food Agric.*, **30**, 843–8.)

the digestion of proteins and carbohydrates. A decrease in the activities of peptidases and disaccharidases in the intestinal mucosa of animals fed raw legumes or purified lectins has indeed been observed. Disruption of the normal protein-, fat- and carbohydrate-intermediary metabolism may, in addition, be due to hormone mimicking effects of the lectins on endocrine cells.

It has been known for a long time that feeding of rats with diets containing raw soybeans and soybean oil meal (the protein rich cake remaining after extraction of the oil from the seeds) results in poorer than normal growth rates, as well as other deleterious effects such as enlargement of the pancreas and depressed serum insulin levels. Most of these effects are due to the inhibitors of proteolytic enzymes (mainly trypsin inhibitors) present in the seeds, but to what extent they may be ascribed to the lectins, such as soybean agglutinin, is still not certain. It has been found, for instance, that selective removal of the lectin from soybean oil meal did not improve the growth of animals fed with this meal [25]. On the other hand it was reported that feeding of rats with diets to which purified soybean lectin has been added depressed the growth of the animals, and induced pancreas enlargement [27a].

Experiments with PHA have shown that an appreciable amount of the lectin crossed the intestinal barrier and some of it gained access to the blood stream and stimulated the production of anti-PHA antibodies. In the small intestines of rat and chicks fed diets containing raw beans or the purified bean lectins, an overgrowth of coliform bacteria occurred. This has been ascribed to the ability of lectins to bind to both the intestinal cells and bacteria, thus serving as a ‘glue’ for the attachment of increased numbers of bacteria to the intestine. A combination of these and other effects may influence the utilization of diets and the growth and health of animals. To what extent this is also true for humans is not known, since no experimental work has been done on the effects of lectins in human diet.

CHAPTER 5
Carbohydrate specificity

Studies of the carbohydrate specificity of lectins are customarily performed by the hapten inhibition technique, in which different monosaccharides, oligosaccharides, or glycopeptides, are tested for their ability to inhibit either haemagglutination (Fig. 3.1) or polysaccharide (or glycoprotein) precipitation by the lectin. This technique stems from the observation of Landsteiner, made in the early part of the century, that a simple substance with a structure closely related to, or identical to, the immunological determinant group of an antigen can combine with the antibody and thereby competitively inhibit the antigen–antibody reaction (Fig. 1.1). Such inhibition studies are possible also with lectins because the binding of sugars to lectins is relatively weak, does not result in the formation of covalent bonds, and is reversible, like the reaction of an antibody with an antigen (or of an enzyme with an inhibitor). The compound that inhibits at the lowest concentration is assumed to be most complementary to the combining site of the lectin.

Since the reaction between a lectin and a saccharide is a reversible equilibrium process, represented by

$$\text{lectin} + \text{sugar} \rightleftharpoons \text{lectin–sugar complex}$$

$$L + S \rightleftharpoons LS$$

$$K_a = \frac{[LS]}{[L] \times [S]},$$

it can also be examined by physicochemical methods, such as spectrophotometry, fluorimetry and nuclear magnetic resonance (NMR). By these methods, the association constant, K_a, and other thermodynamic and kinetic parameters of the reaction can be measured, thus affording information on the binding process between lectins and carbohydrates, and giving a deeper insight into the nature of the combining sites of lectins. Nevertheless, for routine determinations of lectin specificity the less accurate, but much simpler, hapten inhibition technique is of value, in particular since association constants for the interaction of a lectin with a series of carbohydrates correlate well with the relative inhibitory activity of the same sugars.

The binding constants between lectins and monosaccharides, determined by different physicochemical methods, are typically in the range 10^3 to $5 \times 10^4\ \text{M}^{-1}$, and between lectins and oligosaccharides in the range 10^5 to $10^7\ \text{M}^{-1}$. These values are of the same order of magnitude as those for the binding of haptens to antibodies and of substrates to enzymes. For example, the association constants for the binding of *N*-acetylglucosamine and its *β*-linked di- and trisaccharides (chitobiose and chitotriose) with hen egg white lysozyme are 20–50, 5×10^3 and $1 \times 10^5\ \text{M}^{-1}$, respectively.

As mentioned in Chapter 1, lectins are classified into a small number of specificity groups according to the monosaccharide that is the best hapten inhibitor of the lectin. The structures of these monosaccharides are given in Fig. 5.1. Some lectins, however, do not fit into this simple classification since they react almost exclusively with oligosaccharides (section 5.2).

The distribution throughout nature of lectins belonging to the different groups is not uniform (Table 1.1). Lectins specific for galactose (and *N*-acetylgalactosamine) appear to be the most abundant and are present in all classes of organism. These are followed by lectins specific for mannose, which have a somewhat more limited

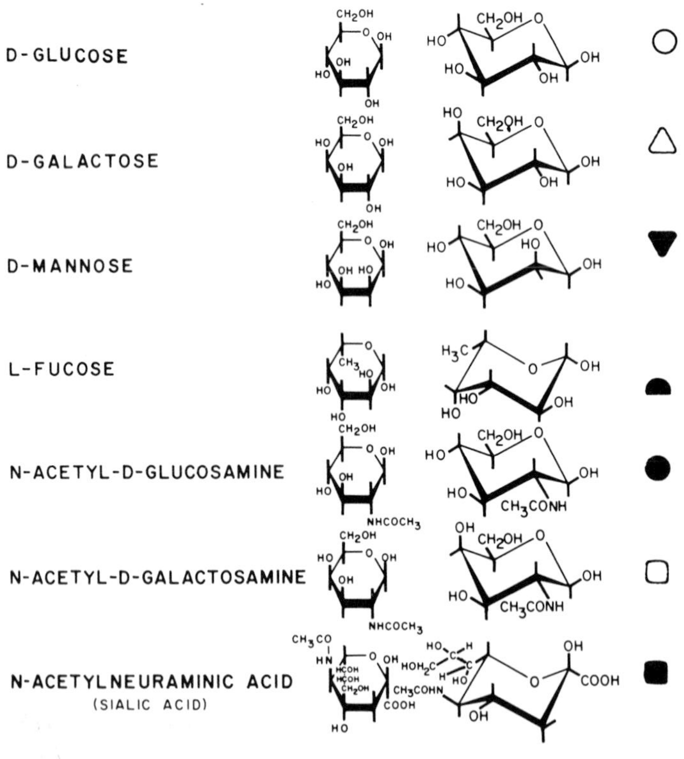
D-GLUCOSE
D-GALACTOSE
D-MANNOSE
L-FUCOSE
N-ACETYL-D-GLUCOSAMINE
N-ACETYL-D-GALACTOSAMINE
N-ACETYLNEURAMINIC ACID
(SIALIC ACID)

Fig. 5.1 Structures of cell surface monosaccharides. In the centre two columns, the formulae of the sugars are drawn in their pyranose forms, according to the Haworth projection (left) and in their stable chair conformation (right). The outer right column shows symbols, used throughout the book, to represent these sugars.

distribution – for example, they have not been found in invertebrates. Lectins specific for sialic acid, on the other hand, are found primarily in invertebrates and viruses, are rare in plants and have not been detected in vertebrates. The lectins within each group may differ markedly in their affinity for the specific monosac-

Table 5.1 Lectins with preference for oligosaccharides

	Specificity		
Lectin	*Monosaccharide*	*Oligosaccharide structure*	*RIA**
Concanavalin A	Man	Manα3(Manα6)Man	130
Datura stramonium	GlcNAc	GlcNAcβ4GlcNAcβ4GlcNAc	550
Dolichos biflorus	GalNAc	GalNAcα3GalNAc	36
Elderberry	Gal	NeuAcα2→3Gal	30–80
		NeuAcα2→6Gal	1600
Erythrina cristagalli	Gal	Galβ4GlcNAc	30–50
Peanut	Gal	Galβ3GalNAc	50
E-PHA	None	Galβ4GlcNAcβ2Manα6╲ GlcNAcβ4 — Manβ4-R† GlcNAcβ2Manα3╱	
L-PHA	None	Galβ4GlcNAcβ6╲ Man Galβ4GlcNAcβ2╱	
Vicia graminea	None	NH₂—Leu | (Galβ3GalNAcα) —Ser | (Galβ3GlcNAcα) —Thr | (Galβ3GalNAcα) —Thr | Glu—COOH	
Vicia villosa	GalNAc	NH₂ | (GalNAcα)— Ser | (Pro)₂ | Gly | (Ala)₂ | (GalNAcα)—Thr—COOH	120
Wheat germ	GlcNAc	GlcNAcβ4GlcNAcβ4GlcNAc	3000

*Relative inhibitory activity with the inhibitory activity of the monosaccharide arbitrarily set as 1.

†R = GlcNAcβ4GlcNAc.

For original literature see reference 2. The data on elderberry are from Shibuya *et al.* [28].

charide or its various derivatives. Moreover, certain lectins interact more strongly with di-, tri- and tetrasaccharides than with monosaccharides (Table 5.1). In such oligosaccharides the monosaccharide for which the lectin is specific is present, usually at the non-reducing end, although there are lectins that also recognize the specific sugar when it occupies an internal position. This point deserves special emphasis, since it is frequently stated that lectins combine only with terminal, non-reducing sugars. For instance, concanavalin A, specific for mannose, binds also internal 2-O-α-substituted mannose residues. *Ricinus communis* agglutinin, specific for galactose, combines with *N*-acetylneuraminyl α2→6 galactose as well, although to a lesser extent; it does not interact, however, with *N*-acetylneuraminyl α2→3 galactose [29]. An extreme case is that of the lectin from human plasma which recognizes only penultimate *β*-galactose residues to which a neutral sugar residue is attached, and does not interact at all with exposed terminal non-reducing galactose residues [30].

5.1 MONOSACCHARIDES

Individual lectins vary considerably in their ability to interact with derivatives or isomers of the monosaccharides for which they are specific. Some lectins possess anomeric specificity, reacting preferentially with either the α or the *β* anomer of the respective monosaccharide (Fig. 5.2), whereas others are devoid of such specificity and interact equally well with both anomers. Thus, concanavalin A and the lectins from *Griffonia simplicifolia* (I-B_4) and *Lotus tetragonolobus* exhibit pronounced specificity for the α-anomers of mannose (or glucose), galactose and L-fucose, respectively, whereas most animal lectins are specific for the *β*-anomers of galactose. On the other hand, the lectins from soybean and *Ricinus communis* are almost completely devoid of anomeric specificity. The nature of the glycoside may markedly influence its interaction with a lectin. In particular aromatic glycosides (e.g. those containing the phenyl or *p*-nitrophenyl group) bind to many lectins much more strongly than aliphatic ones (e.g. ethyl or methyl), attesting to the presence of a hydrophobic region close to the carbohydrate combining site.

Many lectins tolerate some variations at the C-2 position of the sugar to which they bind. Thus, most lectins specific for mannose combine well with glucose and,

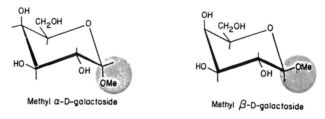

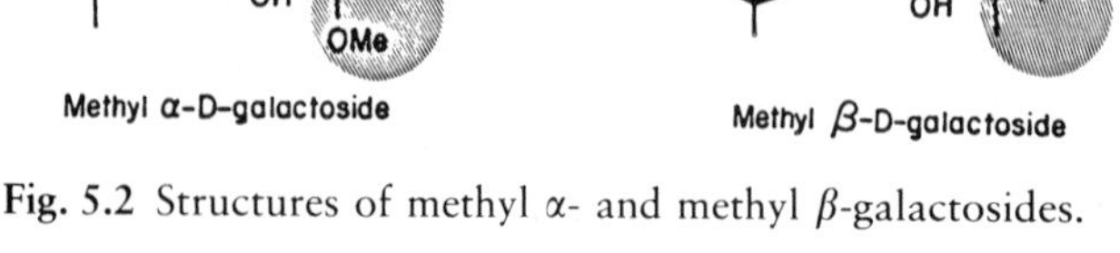
OH
CH2OH
O
HO
OH
OMe
Methyl α-D-galactoside
OH
CH2OH
O
HO
OH
OMe
Methyl β-D-galactoside

Fig. 5.2 Structures of methyl α- and methyl *β*-galactosides.

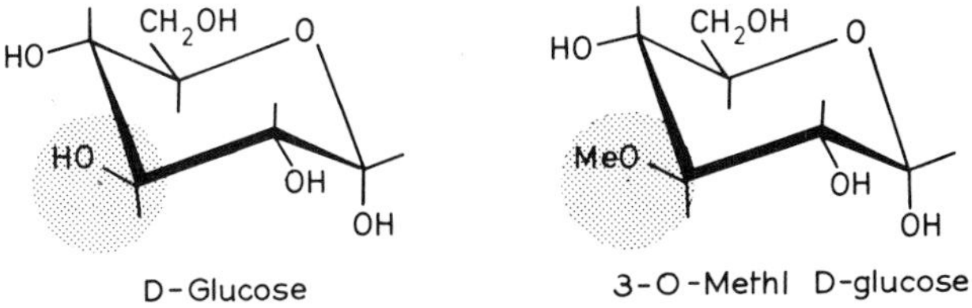
D-Glucose
3-O-Methl D-glucose

Fig. 5.3 Structures of glucose and 3-O-methyl glucose.

to some extent, with *N*-acetylglucosamine. Exceptions are the mannose specific lectins of the snowdrop (*Galanthus nivalis*) [31] and of *Escherichia coli* which do not react at all with glucose. A considerable number of galactose specific lectins react with *N*-acetylgalactosamine and *vice versa*, although others exhibit pronounced preference for only one or the other of these sugars.

Substitution at the C-3 position is tolerated by the lectins from lentil, pea and fava bean (*Vicia faba*), which combine with 3-O-methyl glucose better than with glucose (Fig. 5.3), but not by concanavalin A which binds only poorly to the modified sugar.

The configuration of the 4-hydroxyl group is important for the binding of sugars to lectins, since galactose specific lectins do not react with glucose, nor do lectins specific for glucose react with galactose. This rule does not always apply to lectins that interact with *N*-acetylhexosamines. For example, wheat germ

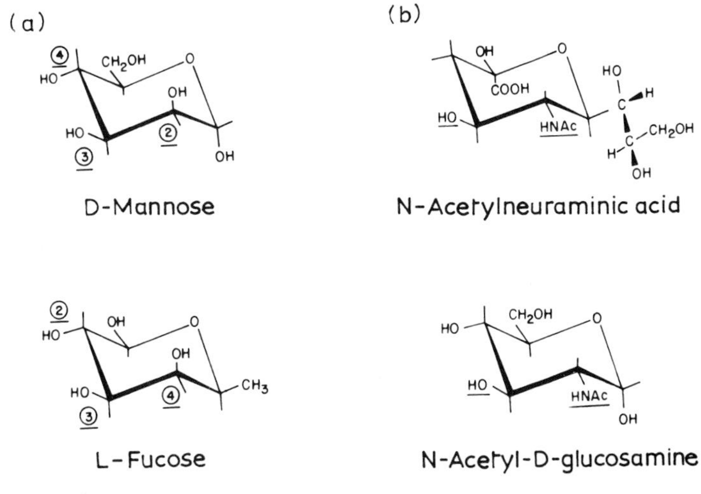
(a)
(b)
D-Mannose
N-Acetylneuraminic acid
L-Fucose
N-Acetyl-D-glucosamine

Fig. 5.4 Common structural features of mannose and L-fucose (a) and of *N*-acetylneuraminic acid and *N*-acetylglucosamine (b). (Groups that occupy the same position in space are underlined.) Rotation of the L-fucose molecule by 180° allows superimposition of its ring oxygen, 4-OH, 3-OH, and 2-OH with the ring oxygen, 2-OH, 3-OH and 4-OH of mannose, respectively. Conformational similarity of *N*-acetyglucosamine and *N*-acetylneuraminic acid at positions C-2 (acetamido group) and C-3 (hydroxyl group) of the pyranose rings is observed when the sialic acid molecule is suitably rotated.

agglutinin, specific for *N*-acetylglucosamine and its oligomers, also binds *N*-acetylgalactosamine, although more weakly, while the blood type A specific, *N*-acetylgalactosamine binding lectin from *Helix pomatia* interacts with *N*-acetylglucosamine as well.

In rare cases, lectins bind to apparently unrelated sugars. Two examples are the lectin from chicken liver and wheat germ agglutinin. The former reacts both with L-fucose and mannose, while the latter reacts with *N*-accetylglucosamine and *N*-acetylneuraminic acid. However, consideration of the three dimensional structures of each pair of these monosaccharides reveals the presence of common features (Fig. 5.4).

Among the lectins specific for sialic acids, some exhibit high affinity for *N*-acetylneuraminic acid, while others react preferentially with 9-*O*-acetyl *N*-acetylneuraminic acid (the lectins from *Cancer antennarius* and of influenza virus C) or *N*-glycolylneuraminic acid (the lectin from *Escherichia coli* K99).

5.2 OLIGOSACCHARIDES

As a result of recent advances in glycoprotein research and synthetic carbohydrate chemistry, numerous oligosaccharides and glycopeptides of known structure became available and have been widely used for probing the combining sites of lectins. These compounds have been particularly helpful in defining the specificity of lectins that react poorly or not at all with monosaccharides (Table 5.1). The minimal structural unit that inhibits L-PHA, the leukoagglutinating isolectin of phytohaemagglutinin, is the disaccharide GlcNAcβ2Man; the most active inhibitor is the pentasaccharide Galβ4GlcNAcβ2(Galβ4GlcNAcβ6)Man (Fig.5.5). The lectins of the mushroom *Agaricus bisporus*, of *Vicia graminea* (specific for blood group N), and of *Vicia villosa* are inhibited better by glycopeptides than by the corresponding oligosaccharides; they thus appear to recognize carbohydrate sequences together with the amino acid or the peptide to which the carbohydrate is linked.

The new oligosaccharides also made it possible to obtain additional information about the specificity of lectins which react well with monosaccharides (Table 5.1). A recent case is concanavalin A, which has been shown to combine 130 times better with the trisaccharide Manα3(Manα6)Man than with methyl α-mannoside. The presence of *N*-acetylglucosamine $\beta 1 \rightarrow 4$ linked to the reducing mannose, (is known as 'bisecting *N*-acetylglucosamine') decreases binding of the oligosaccharide to this lectin by a factor of 10. Two other mannose specific lectins, those from pea and lentil, require L-fucose attached to the innermost asparagine linked *N*-acetylglucosamine residue of glycopeptides and the corresponding oligosaccharides for strong binding. Binding to concanavalin A is not affected by the presence or absence of such L-fucose.

Of the three β-galactose specific lectins from rat lung, one (RL-29) reacts with GalNAcα3(L-Fucα2)Galβ4Glc 2500 times better than with galactose, while the

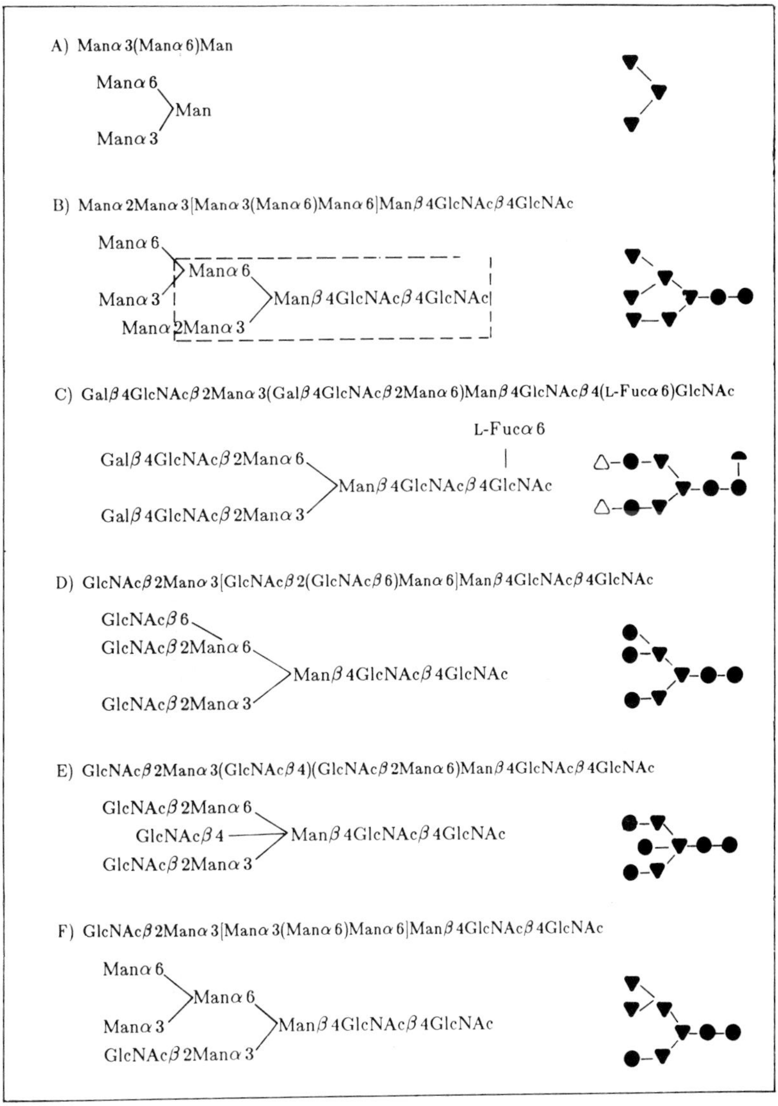

A) Manα3(Manα6)Man
Manα6
Man
Manα3
B) Manα2Manα3[Manα3(Manα6)Manα6]Manβ4GlcNAcβ4GlcNAc
Manα6
Manα6
Manα3
Manβ4GlcNAcβ4GlcNAc
Manα2Manα3
C) Galβ4GlcNAcβ2Manα3(Galβ4GlcNAcβ2Manα6)Manβ4GlcNAcβ4(L-Fucα6)GlcNAc
L-Fucα6
Galβ4GlcNAcβ2Manα6
Manβ4GlcNAcβ4GlcNAc
Galβ4GlcNAcβ2Manα3
D) GlcNAcβ2Manα3[GlcNAcβ2(GlcNAcβ6)Manα6]Manβ4GlcNAcβ4GlcNAc
GlcNAcβ6
GlcNAcβ2Manα6
Manβ4GlcNAcβ4GlcNAc
GlcNAcβ2Manα3
E) GlcNAcβ2Manα3(GlcNAcβ4)(GlcNAcβ2Manα6)Manβ4GlcNAcβ4GlcNAc
GlcNAcβ2Manα6
GlcNAcβ4
Manβ4GlcNAcβ4GlcNAc
GlcNAcβ2Manα3
F) GlcNAcβ2Manα3[Manα3(Manα6)Manα6]Manβ4GlcNAcβ4GlcNAc
Manα6
Manα6
Manα3
Manβ4GlcNAcβ4GlcNAc
GlcNAcβ2Manα3

Fig. 5.5 Different ways of presenting oligosaccharides. For each oligosaccharide, the linear form is given on top and the branched form under it; on the right is a symbolic representation. (A) Mannose trisaccharide; (B) oligomannose unit; the broken line frames the pentasaccharide core common to all *N*-linked oligosaccharides; (C) dibranched (biantennary) complex unit; (D) tribranched complex unit; (E) bisected unit; (F) hybrid unit.

reactivity of the other two lectins (RL-14.5 and RL-18) with the same tetrasaccharide is only about 100 times better than with galactose [32].

Consideration of the oligosaccharide specificity of various lectins has revealed that they can be classified according to the type of carbohydrate unit they recognize.

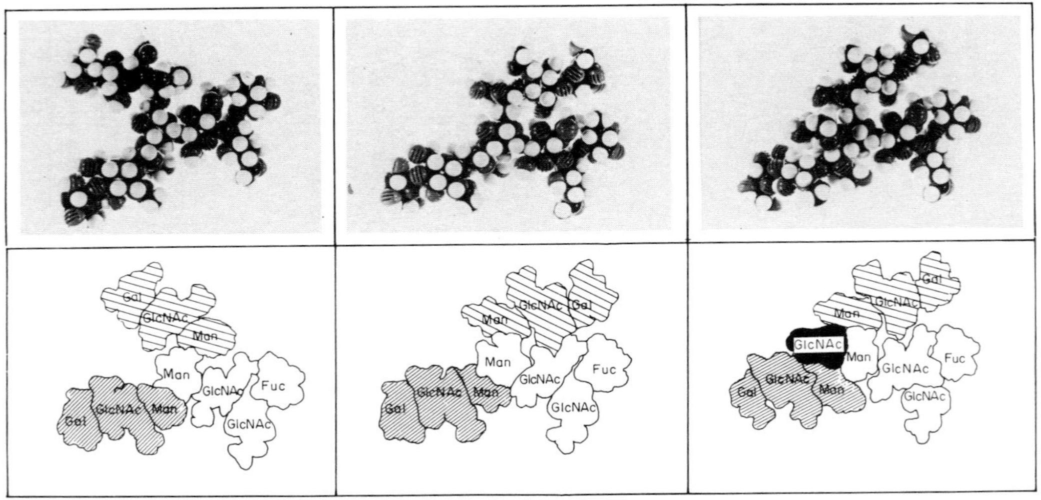
Gal
GlcNAc
Man
Man
GlcNAc
Fuc
Gal
GlcNAc
Man
GlcNAc
Man
GlcNAc
Gal
Man
GlcNAc
Fuc
Gal
GlcNAc
Man
GlcNAc
Gal
GlcNAc
Man
GlcNAc
Man
GlcNAc
Fuc
Gal
GlcNAc
Man
GlcNAc

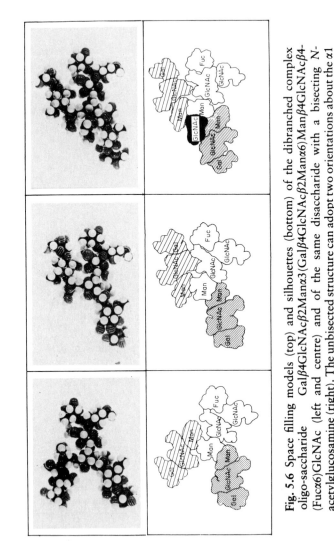

Fig. 5.6 Space filling models (top) and silhouettes (bottom) of the dibranched complex oligo-saccharide Galβ4GlcNAcβ2Manα3(Galβ4GlcNAcβ2Manα6)Manβ4GlcNAcβ4-(Fucα6)GlcNAc (left and centre) and of the same disaccharide with a bisecting *N*-acetylglucosamine (right). The unbisected structure can adopt two orientations about the $\alpha 1 \rightarrow 6$ linkage, whereas the bisected analogue can adopt only a single orientation about this linkage. Fine shaded area, $\alpha 1 \rightarrow 3$ arm; striped area, $\alpha 1 \rightarrow 6$ arm; black area, bisecting *N*-acetylglucosamine. (Modified from Rademacher, T.W., Homans, S.W., Parekh, R.B. and Dwek, R.A. (1986) *Biochem. Soc. Symp.*, **51**, 131–48.) (Photographs of the model courtesy of Raymond A. Dwek.)

Thus, peanut agglutinin and the lectins of *Agaricus bisporus* and *Bauhinia purpurea* react primarily with O-linked (mucin type) sugar units, whereas soybean agglutinin and *Ricinus communis* agglutinin bind *N*-linked (complex) ones.

Rather surprisingly, sugars that are good hapten inhibitors for a given lectin in solution, do not always bind to the same lectin when it is immobilized. Comparison of the behaviour of various glycopeptides on columns of concanavalin A-Sepharose with their association constants with the lectin in solution revealed that only those with association constants higher than $4.5 \times 10^6\ \text{M}^{-1}$ are retained on the columns, while glycopeptides with association constants of $4 \times 10^6\ \text{M}^{-1}$ or less are not retained.

Oligosaccharides are flexible molecules that may assume different shapes, because there is considerable freedom of rotation around the glycosidic bonds connecting the individual monosaccharide constituents [33, 34]. Molecular modelling, as well as high resolution NMR studies of oligosaccharides in solution, have shown that the shape of an oligosaccharide dictates its ability to combine with a lectin. In the oligosaccharide Manα3(Manα6)Manβ4GlcNAcβ4GlcNAc (the pentasaccharide core present in all asparagine linked carbohydrate chains) and its

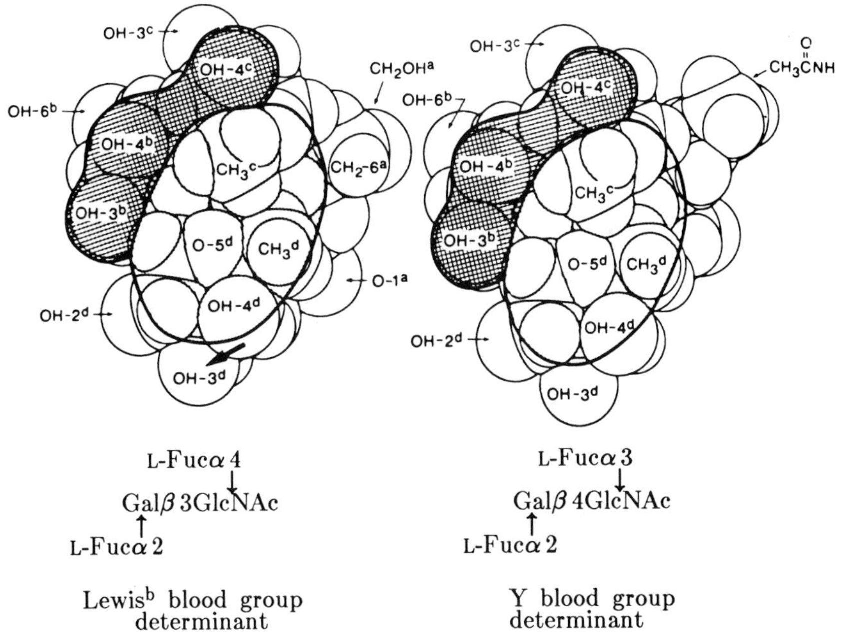
OH-3c
OH-4c
OH-6b
OH-4b
CH3c
CH2OHa
CH2-6a
OH-3b
O-5d
CH3d
O-1a
OH-2d
OH-4d
OH-3d
OH-6b
CH3CNH
L-Fucα 4
Galβ 3GlcNAc
L-Fucα 2
L-Fucα 3
Galβ 4GlcNAc
L-Fucα 2
Lewisb blood group determinant
Y blood group determinant

Fig. 5.7 Computer drawn models (top) and chemical structures (bottom) of the Lewis[b] and Y blood group determinants. The a, b, c and d superscripts refer to atoms on the β-*N*-acetylglucosamine, β-galactose, α1→4 linked L-fucose and α1→2 linked L-fucose units, respectively. The shaded areas represent regions that are bound by *Griffonia simplicifolia* lectin IV. These surfaces are present in both tetrasaccharides, which react almost equally well with the lectin. (Reproduced with permission from Spohr, U., Hindsgaul, O. and Lemieux, R.U. (1985) *Can. J. Chem.*, 63, 2644–52.)

derivative (Fig.5.5) the $\alpha 1 \rightarrow 6$ linked mannose can form two rotational isomers relative to the C5–C6 bond of the $\beta 1 \rightarrow 4$ linked mannose of the core (Fig.5.6). The prevalence of either of the two isomers depends on the type of substitution on the mannose residues of the core. In particular, attachment of a bisecting *N*-acetylglucosamine fixes the orientation of the Manα6Man arm into one of the two possible conformations and, as mentioned above, markedly decreases the binding of the oligosaccharide to concanavalin A.

Because of their flexibility, oligosaccharides that differ in their chemical structure may have substantial topographic features in common. For example, this explains why the two tetrasaccharides shown in Fig. 5.7 bind equally well to *Griffonia simplicifolia* lectin IV in spite of the considerable structural differences between them [35].

CHAPTER 6
Molecular properties

Lectins constitute a heterogeneous group of proteins with a wide range of molecular properties. Indeed, there are no structural features common to all of them, except that they are proteins and that they consist of subunits or protomers. Their molecular weights range from 8500 Da (the lectin from stinging nettle stems) to 400 000 Da (*Limulus polyphemus* lectin). Some lectins are very unusual in their composition and structure. Striking examples are the lectins from potato, tomato and *Datura stramonium* (all members of the *Solanceae* family), which are glycoproteins with a high content of L-arabinose and also contain the rarely occurring amino acid hydroxyproline. Another unusual lectin is wheat germ agglutinin which is particularly rich in disulphide bonds.

6.1 SUBUNIT STRUCTURE

Lectins usually consist of two or four subunits, although the number may be as high as 20 (for the *Limulus polyphemus* lectin) or more. In most cases the subunits are identical, and each of them contains a single sugar binding site with the same specificity. They are usually made up of single polypeptide chains, but subunits composed of two polypeptide chains are also known. An example of the latter type are the lectins of the Viciae tribe of the legume family, such as the pea, lentil and fava bean lectins, each of which contains light α chains (MW 5000–7000 Da) and heavy β chains (MW 15 000–17 000 Da). Each subunit of these lectins consists of one α and one β chain, so that their overall structure can be depicted as $(\alpha\beta)_2$.

A different type of subunit heterogeneity was first demonstrated in concanavalin A. The highly purified crystalline lectin is composed of a mixture of intact subunits made up of a single polypeptide chain containing 237 amino acids and of 'nicked' subunits in which the same polypeptide chain is split into two fragments between residues 118 and 119. The biological activities and the three dimensional structure of concanavalin A, made up of four intact subunits or of a mixture of intact and nicked subunits, are essentially the same; the two forms of the lectin, however, differ slightly in their solubility and affinity for Sephadex. Nicked subunits are also found in several other lectins, e.g. soybean and fava bean agglutinins.

6.2 ISOLECTINS

Careful examination of purified lectins often reveals that they consist of a group of closely related proteins known as isolectins. Typically, isolectins have a similar molecular structure, although they may differ slightly in their carbohydrate specificity or some physical property such as electric charge. They can, therefore, be separated by ion exchange chromatography (Fig. 6.1) or by affinity chromatography on immobilized sugars. The relative proportions of the isoforms of a particular lectin may vary between different species of the same plant, suggesting that their synthesis is under genetic control. This is nicely demonstrated in the case of wheat germ agglutinin, which consists of two subunits, either identical (homomeric) or slightly different (heteromeric). Altogether, four types of subunit are known, each of which is the product of a distinct genome (Table 6.1). In diploid wheat, a single subunit species is present giving rise to only one molecular form of the lectin. In polyploids, however, the different polypeptide chains, coded for by the different genomes, combine randomly with identical or non-identical partners, forming both homodimers and heterodimers in all possible combinations. Because of their great similarity it is not surprising that the subunits of wheat germ isolectins can also be interchanged *in vitro*. Moreover, the subunits of lectins from different cereals (wheat, rye and barley) can be exchanged to form intergeneric, heteromeric lectins. The lectins from these three plants are indeed similar in their physicochemical properties and carbohydrate specificity.

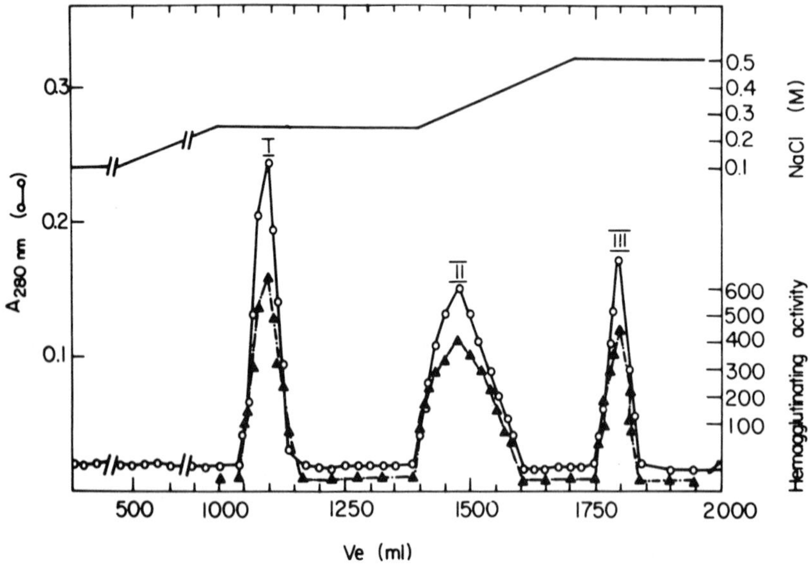
A280 nm
0.3
0.2
0.1
I
II
III
0.5
0.4
0.3
0.2
0.1
NaCl (M)
600
500
400
300
200
100
Hemagglutinating activity (units/ml)
500
1000
1250
1500
1750
2000
Ve (ml)

Fig. 6.1 Separation of wheat germ isolectins (I, II and III) by ion exchange chromatography on a column of SP-Sephadex C-25. Elution was performed by increasing sodium chloride concentration as indicated in the upper part of the figure. ○—○, protein; ▲—▲, haemagglutinating activity; Ve–elution volume (Courtesy of Reuben Lotan.)

Table 6.1 Correlation between wheat genome and subunit composition of wheat germ isolectins*

Genome	*Ploidity*	*Subunits*	*Isolectins*
AA	di	A	AA
DD	di	D	DD
AAGG	tetra	A; G	AA; GG; AG
AABB	tetra	A; B	AA; BB; AB
AABBDD	hexa	A; B; D	AA; AB; AD
			BB; BD; DD

*Not all of the possible isolectin forms have been found.

The group I lectins from *Griffonia simplicifolia* consist of a family of five isolectins, each a tetramer of one or two types of subunit A and B (Fig. 6.2) which are very similar in molecular size and amino acid composition. The structure of the five isolectins can be represented as A_4, A_3B_1, A_2B_2, A_1B_3 and B_4. Subunit A is specific for α-*N*-acetylgalactosamine (but also reacts with α-galactose), whereas subunit B is specific for α-galactose only. The structure of *Griffonia simplicifolia* isolectins is analogous to that of PHA isolectins, which also represent a family of five tetrameric proteins with varying proportions of two classes of subunit, E and L. The PHA isolectins differ in their biological properties: E_4 (E-PHA) is a potent haemagglutinin, L_4 (L-PHA) has leukoagglutinating activity (i.e. the ability to agglutinate white blood cells such as lymphocytes) and is a potent mitogen; intermediate forms (e.g. E_2L_2 or E_3L_1) possess lower levels of the above activities. E_4 and L_4 also differ in their specificity for oligosaccharides. The lectin from *Datura stramonium* seeds has recently been separated into three individual isolectins, two of which are homodimers made up of two A or two B subunits, whereas the third is a heterodimer composed of one A and one B subunit [36]. The A and B subunits differ slightly in their molecular weights (32 000 Da and 28 000 Da, respectively), amino acid composition and carbohydrate specificity. The A subunit has a higher affinity for $\beta 1 \rightarrow 4$ linked oligomers of *N*-acetylglucosamine than the B subunit, whereas the latter binds more strongly to certain glycoproteins, especially ovomucoid.

The two types of lectin found in the seeds of *Ricinus communis* and of *Abrus precatorius* can be considered as special cases of isolectins. These plants each contain a weakly agglutinating toxin (ricin and abrin, respectively), and a non-toxic

A A
A A
B A
A A
B B
A A
B B
B A
B B
B B

Fig. 6.2 The tetrameric structure of the five isoforms of *Griffonia simplicifolia* lectin I. A and B denote the two types of subunit of the lectin.

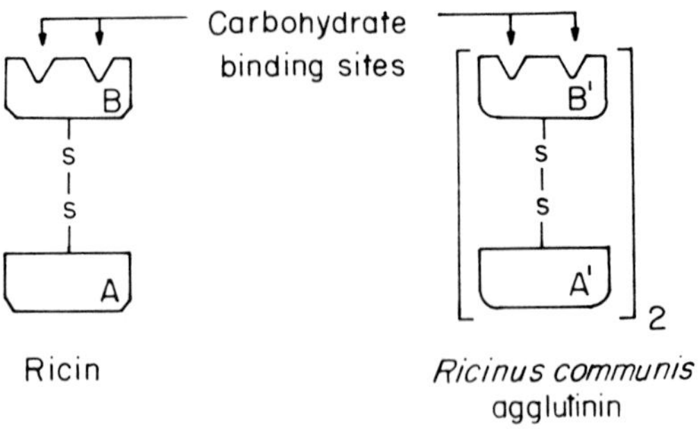
Carbohydrate
binding sites
B
S
S
A
B'
S
S
A'
2
Ricin
Ricinus communis
agglutinin

Fig. 6.3 Structures of ricin and *Ricinus communis* agglutinin.

agglutinin. The agglutinins are tetramers consisting of two toxin-like heterodimers composed of disulphide linked A and B chains; the dimers are held together by non-covalent forces (Fig. 6.3). The corresponding subunits of the toxins and agglutinins are closely related structurally and serologically but differ slightly in their carbohydrate specificities in that the agglutinins bind only galactose and in contrast to the toxins do not bind *N*-acetylgalactosamine. There are also differences in their specificities for oligosaccharides [29].

6.3 METALS IN LECTINS

Most lectins examined, in particular those from the legumes, contain metal ions (as a rule Mn^{2+} and/or Ca^{2+}), and in some cases evidence has been presented for the requirement of the metals for activity. However, only with concanavalin A has the role of metal ions been investigated in detail. The fully active lectin contains Mn^{2+} and Ca^{2+} ions, one of each per subunit, at two distinct sites, S1 and S2, respectively. Demetalized concanavalin A does not bind carbohydrates at all. To convert it to an active form, the metal ions must be added in a prescribed order: first Mn^{2+} (or another divalent transition metal ion), and then Ca^{2+}. The Mn^{2+} binds at site S1 and thus engenders the formation of the specific Ca^{2+} binding site S2; only when both metal binding sites are occupied does the lectin bind sugars. Conformational studies using various physicochemical methods have led to the conclusion that the binding of Ca^{2+} causes an alteration in the environment of the transition metal site which, in turn, is important for the creation and stabilization of the saccharide binding site.

Another type of metal requirement for activity has been observed with mammalian membrane-bound lectins, as well as with some invertebrate lectins, e.g. that of *Limulus polyphemus*. In these lectins, the presence of tightly bound metal has not been demonstrated, but they require the addition of Ga^{2+} ions for activity.

6.4 LECTINS AS GLYCOPROTEINS

With a few exceptions (e.g. concanavalin A, wheat germ agglutinin and peanut agglutinin, which are devoid of covalently bound sugar), most lectins are glycoproteins, some of which contain up to 50% carbohydrate. It appears, however, that the carbohydrate is not required for the sugar binding or biological activities of the glycoprotein lectins since these activities were retained, even after the sugar was modified or removed from the protein by chemical or enzymatic means. Conclusive evidence on this point was obtained recently when it was shown that L-PHA synthesized in *E. coli*, although unglycosylated, had the same leukoagglutinating and mitogenic activity as the glycosylated lectin isolated from red kidney beans [37].

Structural studies of the carbohydrate units of glycoprotein lectins have contributed to our knowledge of glycoproteins in general. On the basis of carbohydrate composition, two types of glycoprotein lectins can be discerned: (a) those containing mainly *N*-acetylglucosamine and mannose (with or without L-fucose and xylose), as exemplified by many of the legume lectins; (b) those containing L-arabinose and galactose, as is the case with potato and tomato lectins. Soybean agglutinin was the first lectin for which the structure of the carbohydrate unit was unequivocally established (Table 6.2). The structure is identical with that of the *N*-linked $Man_9GlcNAc_2$ oligosaccharide found in animal glycoproteins, and nearly identical with the core portion of yeast mannans. The occurrence of the same oligosaccharide in such diverse organisms provides strong evidence for the evolutionary conservation of *N*-linked oligomannose units and concurs with the finding of a common biosynthetic pathway of protein *N*-glycosylation in animals, plants and yeasts.

Many legume lectins contain L-fucose and xylose in addition to mannose and *N*-acetylglucosamine; oligosaccharides containing these four monosaccharides together have not been found in animal or yeast glycoproteins. Investigations of the carbohydrate units of a number of these lectins, carried out very recently

Table 6.2 *N*-Glycosidic carbohydrate units of glycoprotein lectins

Source of lectin	*Structure of carbohydrate chain*
Soybean	Manα2Manα6↘ Manα6↘ Manα2Manα3↗ Manβ4GlcNAcβ4GlcNAc Manα2Manα2Manα3↗
Erythrina cristagalli *Sophora japonica* *Vicia graminea*	Manα6↘ Manβ4GlcNAcβ4GlcNAc *Manα3*↗ ↑β2 ↑α3 Xyl L-Fuc

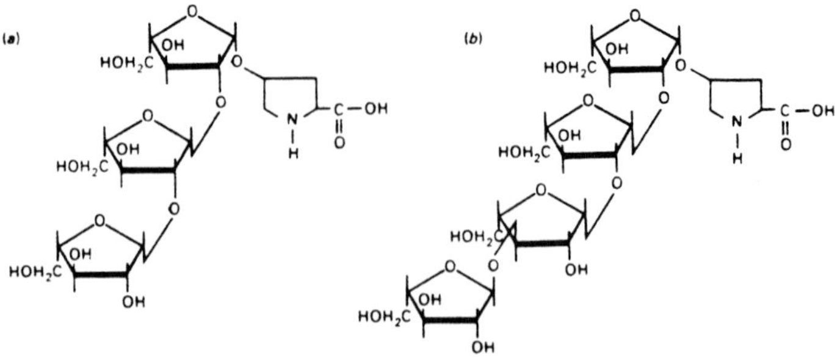
(a)
HOH2C
OH
O
O
O
N
C—OH
O
H
HOH2C
OH
HOH2C
OH
OH
(b)
HOH2C
OH
O
N
C—OH
H
O
HOH2C
OH
HOH2C
OH
HOH2C
OH
OH

Fig. 6.4 Proposed structures for the hydroxyprolyl arabinosides of potato lectin: (a) hydroxyprolyl tri-arabinoside; (b) hydroxyprolyl tetra-arabinoside. (Reproduced with permission from Ashford, D., *et al.* (1982) *Biochem. J.*, **201**, 199–208, copyright © 1982, The Biochemical Society, London.)

[38], have shown that they have the common structure Manα3(Manα6)(Xylβ2)Manβ4GlcNAcβ4(Fucα3)GlcNAc (Table 6.2). This heptasaccharide shows the twin characteristics of a newly established family of *N*-linked glycans, found to date only in plants. The characteristics are substitution of the pentasaccharide core by (a) a xylose residue linked $\beta 1 \rightarrow 2$ to the β-mannosyl residue, and (b) an L-fucose residue linked $\alpha 1 \rightarrow 3$ to the reducing terminal *N*-acetylglucosamine residue.

Lectins containing L-arabinose and galactose seem to be confined to plants of the Solanaceae family. In these, as well as in other plant glycoproteins, the arabinose is in the uncommon furanose (five membered ring) form, rather than in the commonly occurring pyranose (six membered ring) form. Both the potato and the *Datura stramonium* lectins contain the tri- and tetra-arabinofuranosides (L-Ara*f*α3)$_{0-1}$ L-Ara*f*α2L-Ara*f*α2L-Ara*f* β-linked to hydroxyproline (Fig.6.4). The galactose is α-linked to serine of the polypeptide backbone. Neither the arabinofuranosyl–hydroxyproline linking group, nor the galactosyl–serine one has been found in animal glycoproteins.

6.5 PRIMARY STRUCTURES AND HOMOLOGIES

During the last few years, the primary sequences of many lectins have been established, either by conventional methods (using the protein sequenator and various proteolytic cleavages) or by deduction from the nucleotide sequence of the DNA (cDNA) prepared by reverse transcription of the lectin mRNA. Comparison of the sequences has revealed the existence of several families of homologous lectins. The most thoroughly studied of these are the legume lectins, in which close to a dozen complete sequences are known, as well as numerous partial ones. Other families, on which sequence information is available, are the soluble β-galactose specific vertebrate lectins, the liver membrane lectins, and several of the bacterial surface lectins.

6.5.1 Legume lectins

Both the one chain and two chain legume lectins exhibit extensive homologies when properly aligned, i.e. by placing the β chains of the two chain lectins along the NH_2-terminal sequences of the one chain lectins, followed by the α chains, and assuming that at selected positions in the polypeptide chain of one or another lectin individual amino acids (or short peptides) may be missing (Fig. 6.5). Concanavalin A and the lectin from *Dioclea grandiflora*, both belonging to the Diocleae tribe, occupy a special position. In these cases homology with the other legume lectins is obtained by aligning the NH_2-terminal amino acids of the legume lectins with residue 123 of the Diocleae lectins, proceeding to the carboxyl ends of the latter

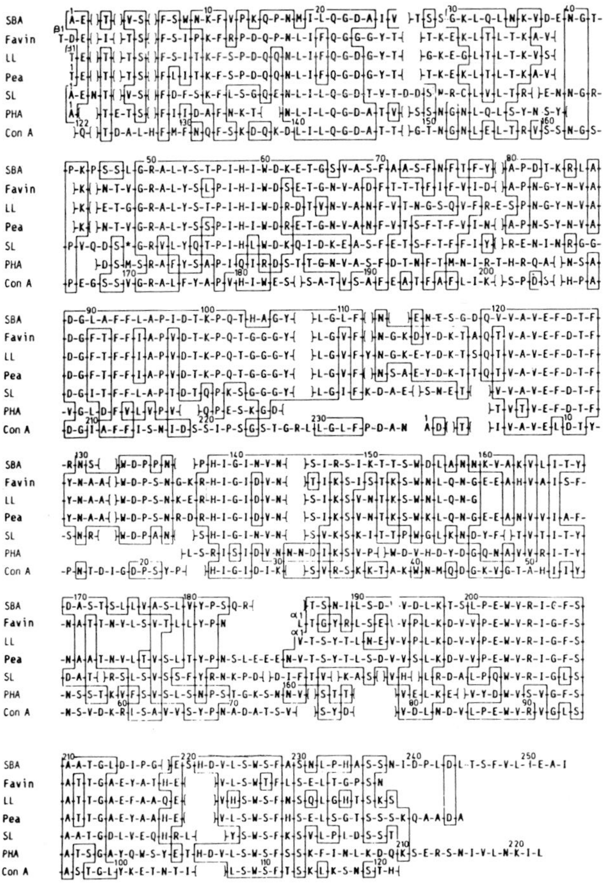
SBA
Favin
LL
Pea
SL
PHA
Con A

Fig. 6.5 Sequence homologies of legume lectins from, soybean (SBA), fava bean (favin), lentil (LL), pea, sainfoin seed (SL), *Phaseolus vulgaris* (PHA), and jack bean (Con A). Numbers above the sequences correspond to the amino acid residues in SBA, except for Con A which is separately numbered. (Modified from Strosberg, A.D., Buffard, D., Lauwereys, M. and Foriers, A. (1986) in reference 1, pp. 249–64.)

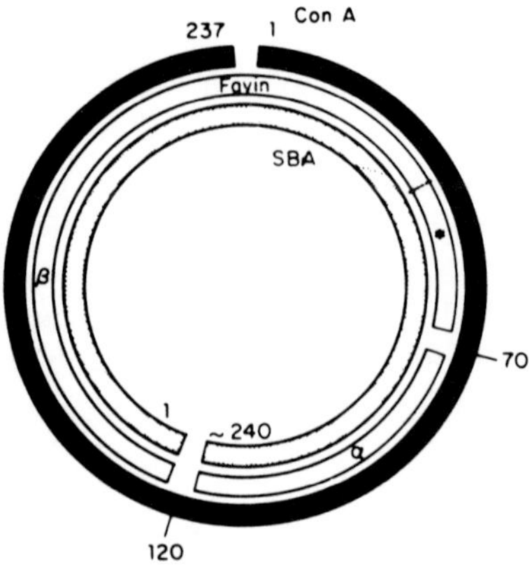
Con A
237
1
Favin
SBA
β
70
1
~240
α
120

Fig. 6.6 Alignment of the primary sequences of fava bean lectin (favin), soybean agglutinin (SBA) and concanavalin A (Con A), showing the circular homology among the sequences of these lectins. (Reproduced with permission from Hemperly, J.J. and Cunningham, B.A. (1983) *Trends Biochem. Sci.*, 8, 100–2.)

and continuing along their NH_2 terminal regions. This unusual type of homology has been referred to as 'circular homology' (Fig. 6.6); shown recently, it is the result of a special step that occurs in the last stage of the biosynthesis of concanavalin A (Chapter 8).

In all legume lectins examined, several positions are invariant or highly conserved (cf. Fig. 6.5). In a number of other position, only conservative substitutions (i.e. by chemically similar residues) occur, for example tyrosine may be substituted by phenylalanine and leucine by isoleucine or valine. It is notable that three of the conserved amino acids (Glu^8, Asp^{19} and His^{24} in the concanavalin A numbering correspond to residues previously identified in concanavalin A as participating directly in the binding of Ca^{2+} and Mn^{2+}. The amino acid residues that constitute the sugar binding site in concanavalin A are replaced by different ones in other mannose binding legume lectins. This observation may account for the fine differences in the carbohydrate specificities of these lectins (section 5.1).

6.5.2 Cereal and Solanaceae lectins

The complete amino acid sequence of only one cereal (*Graminea*) lectin, i.e. wheat germ agglutinin, has been established. Among its many unusual properties, it exhibits a high degree of internal sequence homology between several parts of the molecule. This was expected from the X-ray crystallographic studies (section 7.2) which preceded the sequencing of wheat germ agglutinin and showed that the subunit of this lectin consists of four isostructural domains, each stabilized by four homologously placed disulphide bonds. Comparison of the amino acid sequences has revealed that isolectins 1 and 2 (subunit composition AA and DD, respectively) differ in four amino acids, while isolectin 3 (subunit composition BB) differs from isolectins 1 and 2 in ten and eight amino acids, respectively [39, 41]. It is likely that the lectins from rye and barley have similar primary sequences, since their physicochemical properties are similar to those of wheat germ agglutinin and the subunits of all three lectins are interchangeable. The cereal lectins thus represent a group of proteins which were subjected to only minor changes during the process of divergence from a common ancestor.

Similarly, the lectins from *Solanaceae* plants may have been derived from a common ancestor since they, too, exhibit great similarities in their carbohydrate specificity, their amino acid and carbohydrate composition and possibly also in their three dimensional structures. The lectins from both potato and *Datura stramonium* appear to consist of two dissimilar domains: one contains all the carbohydrate and hydroxyproline of the lectin but none of the cysteine; the other is carbohydrate free (Fig. 6.7). The hydroxyproline residues are all substituted with L-arabinose; some of the serine residues are substituted with galactose. Further evidence for the similarity of the two lectins comes from immunological studies showing that the *Datura stramonium* lectin cross reacts with anti-potato lectin antiserum.

The non-glycosylated domains of the potato and *Datura stramonium* lectins, which are assumed to contain the saccharide binding sites, have high proportions of glycine and cysteine; all of the latter residues are in the disulphide form, so that the domain is highly crosslinked. A high content of glycine and of disulphide bonds is also characteristic of wheat germ agglutinin, which contains 16 disulphide bridges per subunit of 164 amino acids. It has been postulated that extensive homology exists in the primary structure of this lectin with the non-glycosylated domain of the potato lectin, in spite of the fact that they are derived from plants belonging to different families. The assumption that the *Solanaceae* and cereal

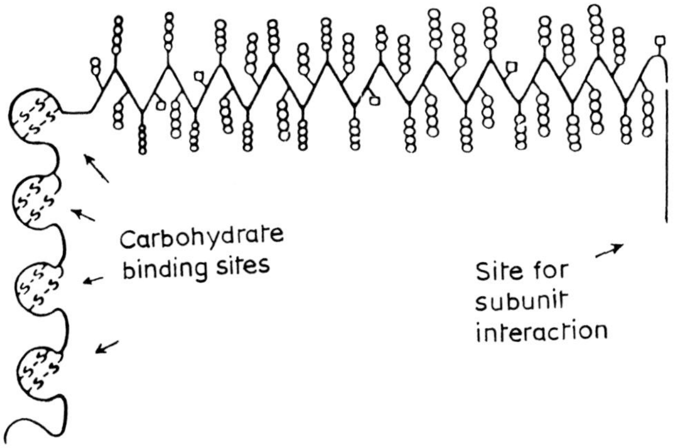
Carbohydrate binding sites
Site for subunit interaction

Fig. 6.7 Hypothetical model of the structure of potato lectin: ○, Arabinofuranoside; □, galactopyranoside. (Reproduced with permission from Allen, A.K. (1983) in: *Chemical Taxonomy, Molecular Biology, and Function of Plant Lectins* (eds. I.J. Goldstein and M.E. Etzler), Alan R. Liss, New York, pp. 71–85.)

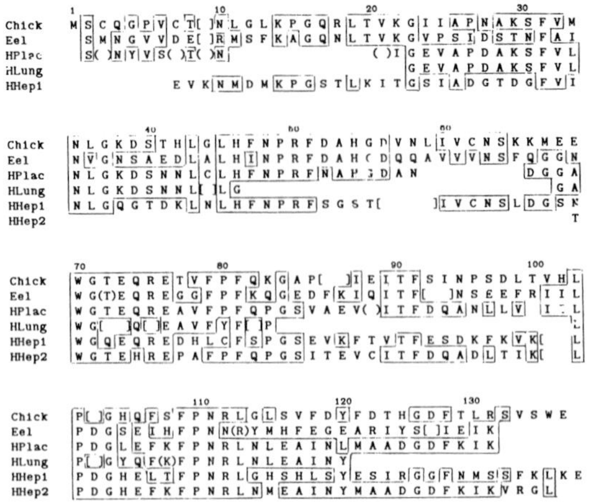

Fig. 6.8 Sequence homology of β-galactose specific vertebrate lectins from chicken embryo skin (Chick), electric eel (Eel), human placenta (HPlac), lung (HLung) and hepatoma (HHepl and HHep2). (Modified from Paroutaud, P., Levi, G., Teichberg, V.I. and Strosberg, A.D. (1987) *Proc. Natl. Acad. Sci. USA*, **84**, 6345–8.)

lectins are structurally similar is supported by the similarity in their carbohydrate specificities; both families of lectins have extended sites complementary to $\beta 1 \rightarrow 4$ linked oligosaccharides of *N*-acetylglucosamine.

6.5.3 β-Galactose specific lectins of vertebrates

All vertebrates synthesize soluble and membrane bound lectins specific for β-galactose. The soluble lectins are readily extracted from the tissues with lactose solutions in the absence of detergents. They share many properties, such as antigenic crossreactivity and requirement for reducing agents for activity. Most of these lectins have a small subunit with a molecular weight of 13 000–17 000 Da, although in some tissues lectins with higher subunit molecular weight occur. Thus, human lung tissue contains several β-galactose specific lectins with subunits of molecular weight 14 000, 22 000 and 29 000 Da. Considerable sequence homologies exist between the β-galactose specific lectins of chick embryo, human lung and electric eel (Fig. 6.8).

6.5.4 Membrane lectins of vertebrates

The membranes of many cells, e.g. hepatocytes and macrophages, contain lectins specific for sugars such as galactose, mannose and *N*-acetylglucosamine, or L-fucose. The galactose binding lectin from rabbit liver, the first animal lectin described, has a molecular weight of 260 000 Da; it consists of two different subunits with apparent molecular weights of 48 000 and 40 000 Da. The *N*-acetylglucosamine specific hepatic lectin from chicken liver is a hexamer of a single subunit species of molecular weight 26 000 Da (Fig. 6.9).

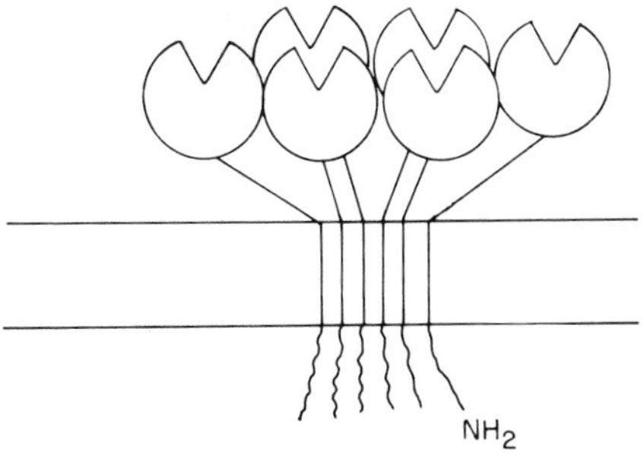
Carbohydrate-recognition domain
Membrane-spanning hydrophobic stretch
Cytoplasmic tail
NH2

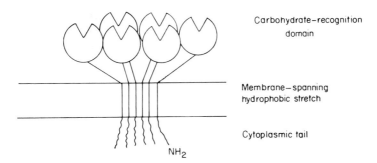

Fig. 6.9 Arrangement of chicken hepatic lectin in the membrane. The molecule consists of six subunits, each with an independent carbohydrate-recognition domain. (Modified from Drickamer, K., Dordal, M.S. and Reynolds, L. (1986) *J. Biol. Chem.*, **261**, 6878–87.)

The membrane bound lectins are anchored to the cell by a membrane spanning stretch of hydrophobic amino acids and an NH_2-terminal cytoplasmic tail. They exhibit extensive homologies, particularly in the COOH-terminal carbohydrate binding domain [10a, 42]. In this domain, which consists of about 130 amino acids, approximately 18 are invariant. Such a pattern of conserved amino acids is found in a number of other proteins not previously known to display carbohydrate binding activity. They include the core protein of cartilage and fibroblast proteoglycan, the lymphocyte Fc receptor and the lung surfactant glycoprotein from the surface of alveoli. Indeed, the lung surfactant glycoprotein has very recently been found to bind carbohydrates in a Ca^{2+} dependent manner.

In addition to the lectins mentioned above, mammalian cells contain two membrane lectins specific for mannose 6-phosphate, one of MW 215 000 Da and one of MW 46 000 Da. Both show similar, but not identical, specificities towards various types of phosphorylated oligosaccharides. The larger lectin has an extracellular domain containing at least ten homologous repeats of approximately 145 amino acids [43]. The most highly conserved region within the repeat consists of a stretch of 13 amino acids that contains cysteine at both ends. The similar length and overall homology of the repeats suggests that they arose from the duplication of a single ancestral sequence. The entire extracellular domain of the low molecular weight lectin is homologous to the 145 amino acid repeat and contains the conserved 13 amino acid segment. These conserved sequences may therefore be essential for a function common to both lectins, probably ligand binding.

6.5.5 Invertebrate lectins

The amino acid sequence of the COOH-terminal half of the galactose specific lectin from the coelomic fluid of the sea urchin, *Anthocidaris crassispina*, is highly homologous to that of the carbohydrate recognition domain of the mannose binding protein from rat liver, as well as several other hepatic lectins [44]. It is also homologous to the central portion of the lectin from the haemolymph of the flesh fly, *Sarcophaga peregrina*. The remarkable homology between the carbohydrate binding domains of vertebrate lectins and parts of invertebrate lectins suggests that these domains appeared relatively early in the evolution of animal lectins.

Not all invertebrate lectins possess common primary sequences: the amino acid sequence of the sialic acid binding lectin from frog (*Rana catesbiana*) eggs is unique and not homologous to any known protein sequence.

6.5.6 Bacterial lectins

Most bacterial lectins occur in the form of fimbriae (pili), filamentous appendages that protrude from the surface of the cells (Fig. 3.3). Their size is usually 5–7 nm in diameter and 100–200 nm in length. The best characterized of these are type 1 (or common) fimbriae of *E. coli* that are mannose specific and type P fimbriae, also of *E. coli*, specific for Galα4Gal. Other examples are type S fimbriae of *E. coli*, specific for NeuAcα2$\rightarrow$3Gal, and type 2 fimbriae of oral Actinomyces, specific for β-galactose. Purified fimbriae each consist of several hundred fimbrillin (or pilin) subunits of different size, mostly of a molecular weight in the range of 15 000–22 000 Da. The major fimbrillin subunits of type 1 fimbriae from different *E. coli* strains have a similar amino acid composition and molecular weight (17 000 Da) and their primary structure is remarkably similar. There are also considerable homologies with the major subunits of fimbriae with other carbohydrate specificities, e.g. type P. Recent work has shown that the major subunits do not possess carbohydrate binding sites; these reside in minor subunit constituents of the fimbriae [45, 46]. The structure of these carbohydrate binding subunits is currently under intensive investigation in various laboratories.

CHAPTER 7
Three dimensional structures

A prerequisite for the complete understanding of the interaction of a lectin with a carbohydrate at the molecular level is a knowledge of the three dimensional structure of the protein, which is best obtained by X-ray crystallography. Many lectins are now being investigated by this method. The structures at high resolution of three legume lectins (concanavalin A, pea lectin and favin), of one cereal lectin (wheat germ agglutinin) and of ricin have so far been elucidated.

7.1 LEGUME LECTINS

In view of the extensive sequence homologies found in the legume lectins, it is not surprising that their tertiary structures are remarkably similar. As originally demonstrated for concanavalin A, the subunit (protomer) of each of the legume lectins examined to date is in the shape of a dome or gumdrop, approximately 42 Å high, 40 Å wide and 30 Å thick (Fig. 7.1). The predominant structural element of each subunit, which accounts for close to half of its amino acid residues, is the arrangement of the polypeptide chains in two anti-parallel pleated sheets (β structures). Most of the residues not included in the β structures are in loops and β bends that connect the strands of the pleated sheets. The remaining residues do not belong to regular secondary structures. One of the pleated sheets runs through the centre of the protomer and is associated with the binding sites for Mn^{2+} and Ca^{2+} ions and for carbohydrates. The other pleated sheet forms the back of the subunit and makes an essential contribution to the interactions between the subunits. The first pleated sheet contains seven anti-parallel chains. The two metal ions are bound at the top of the protomers, between this structure and a loop of two peptide strands that extends from it. The carbohydrate binding site is between this loop and a second peptide loop that also extends from this structure. Several amino acid side chains (Tyr^{12}, Asp^{208} and Arg^{228}) are part of both the Ca^{2+} and the carbohydrate binding sites.

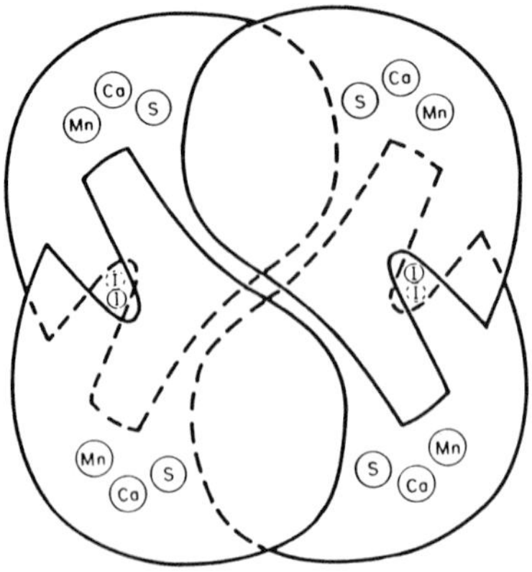
Ca
S
Mn
Ca
S
Mn
Mn
S
Ca
S
Mn
Ca

Fig. 7.1 Schematic representation of concanavalin A tetramer. Ca, Mn and S indicate the positions of Ca^{2+}, Mn^{2+}, and carbohydrate binding sites, respectively. (Reproduced with permission from Becker, J.W., Reeke, G.N.Jr., Cunningham, B.A. and Edelman, G.M. (1976) *Nature*, **259**, 406–9, Copyright © 1976, Macmillan Magazines Ltd.)

The second β structure contains six anti-parallel chains. The naturally occurring cleavage between residues 118 and 119 of some of the molecules of concanavalin A is in a loop between two strands of this β structure and it seems reasonable to expect that the loss of one covalent bond in such a highly stabilized part of the molecule would not disrupt the overall structure in any major way.

Two dome shaped protomers pair to form an ellipsoidal dimer, over 80 Å in length (Fig. 7.1). This dimer is stabilized by hydrogen bonds from the bottom chain of the back β structure of one protomer to the corresponding chain of the back β structure of the second protomer, giving a contiguous 12-chain back pleated sheet which forms the entire back of the dimer. In concanavalin A, each molecule of which consists of four subunits, two such dimers combine to form a tetramer. The tetramer, in the shape of a tetrahedron, is formed by juxtaposing two of the ellipsoid dimers with their 12-chain β structures facing each other. Salt links, hydrogen bonds and hydrophobic interactions involving the side chains projecting from these β structures stabilize the formation of the tetramer. In pea and fava bean lectins that consist of two subunits, no tetramer is formed. Of these three lectins, only favin is a glycoprotein; its carbohydrate moiety is covalently attached to Asn^{168} and projects from the back β structure.

The metal ion and carbohydrate binding sites are very similar in all three legume lectins discussed [47]. Each of the two metal ions (Mn^{2+} and Ca^{2+}) is linked to four protein groups and two water ligands. Two of the side chains belong to aspartic acid residues that are shared by both metal ions (Asp^{10} and Asp^{19}) (Fig. 7.2). The folding of the polypeptide chains in the region of the carbohydrate binding sites is also similar, despite differences in specific amino acid residues.

With both concanavalin A and favin [48], crystals of lectin–saccharide complexes were obtained, which permitted direct crystallographic examination of the carbohydrate binding site. The carbohydrate was located by difference electron

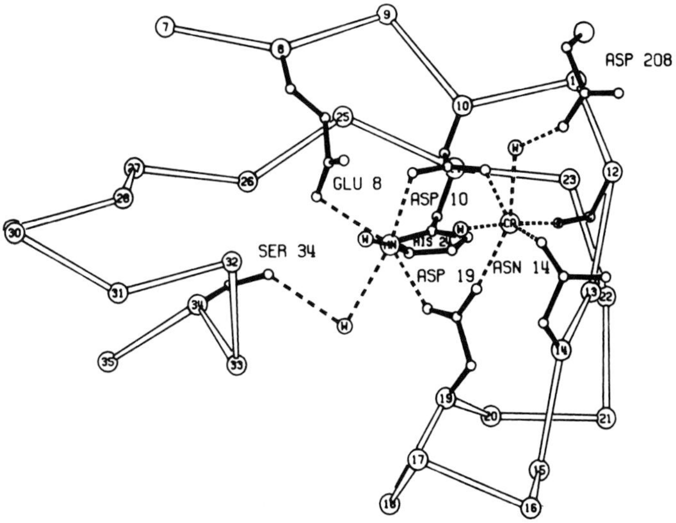
ASP 208
GLU 8
ASP 10
SER 34
HIS 24
ASP 19
ASN 14

Fig. 7.2 Schematic view of the Ca^{2+} and Mn^{2+} binding region in native concanavalin A. The open lines represent virtual bonds between successive α-carbon atoms of residues 7–35. The side-chain ligands are shown as solid lines and the coordination of the metal ions as dashed lines. Water molecules are represented by W. Note that all the direct protein ligands are within the loop of residues 8–24. (Reproduced with permission from Shoham, M., Sussman, J.L., Yonath, A., *et al.* (1978) *FEBS Lett.*, 95, 54–6.)

density techniques at a shallow depression on the protein surface which, in the case of concanavalin A, was at a distance of 12 Å from the Mn^{2+} binding site and 7 Å from the Ca^{2+} binding site. The major structural difference between concanavalin A and favin in the region of the carbohydrate binding site is the replacement of two large side chains, Leu^{99} and Arg^{228} in concanavalin A with smaller groups, Ala^{212} and Gly^{100}, in favin. These replacements make the favin site considerably more open than that of concanavalin A and may account for the fact that substitution of methyl or phenyl groups at C-3 enhances carbohydrate binding by favin but decreases it in concanavalin A.

7.2 WHEAT GERM AGGLUTININ

A high resolution electron density map (up to 1.8 Å [48]) obtained with isolectin 2 shows that wheat germ agglutinin (dimensions 40 × 40 × 70 Å) contains two closely associated subunits of 164 amino acid residues each, centred around the crystallographic two fold axis. Each subunit consists of an assembly of four spatially distinct domains denoted A, B, C and D, each 41 amino acid residues long (Fig. 7.3). The amino acid sequences of the domains are highly homologous. The irregularly folded polypeptide chain of each domain is held in a compact, stable configuration by four disulphide bridges. The half cystines forming the bridges are

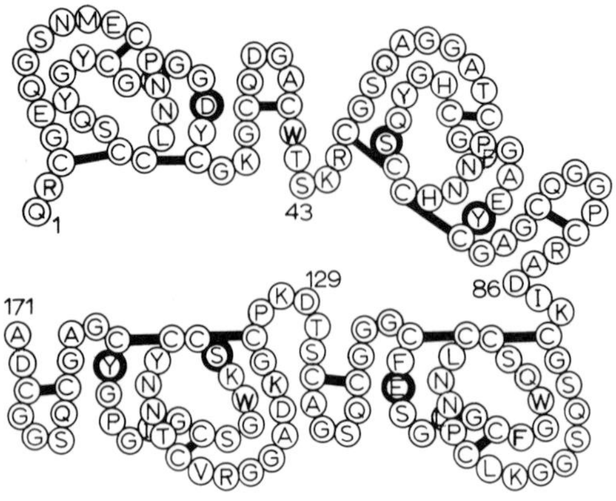
1
43
129
86
171

Fig. 7.3 Diagrammatic representation of the covalent structure of wheat germ agglutinin isolectin 2. Amino acid residues are designated by the standard one-letter code. Disulphide bridges are shown by thick black bars. The residues believed to interact with specific sugar ligands are denoted by circles in heavy outline. (Reproduced with permission from Wright, C.S., Gavilanes, F. and Peterson, D.L. (1984) *Biochemistry*, **23**, 280–7 and private communication.)

spaced three to six residues apart and occur at homologous positions in the four domains. The protein is devoid of the commonly occurring secondary structural elements, the β sheet and α helix. The crystal structure of wheat germ isolectin 2 is very similar to that of isolectin 1, with local differences observed mainly in the B domain of the molecule [39] where three of the four amino acid substitutions between isolectins 1 and 2 are located.

The crystal structures of complexes of wheat germ agglutinin with $\beta 1 \rightarrow 4$ linked di-*N*-acetylglucosamine (*N*, *N*′ diacetylchitobiose) and with *N*-acetylneuraminic acid have been determined from an electron density difference map at 2.8 Å. In both complexes two strong binding sites on the lectin molecule are observed, located in the corresponding crevices at the protomer–protomer interface. The combining sites, are unusual in that they are formed by amino acid side chains of two subunits, i.e. those from the B domain of one protomer and from the C domain of the other. These sites are common for *N*-acetylglucosamine and *N*-acetylneuraminic acid and have been designated primary sites. In addition to the primary sites, two other carbohydrate binding sites were found in the complex of wheat germ agglutinin with *N*, *N*′ diacetylchitobiose, located in the contact region between the A domain of one protomer and the D domain of the other.

7.3 RICIN

The three dimensional structure of ricin has been determined by X-ray crystallography at 2.8 Å resolution [50]. The A chain is a globular protein with extensive secondary structure, both β pleated sheet and α helix, and a reasonably prominent cleft, assumed to be the active site responsible for the toxic action of ricin (section 4.6). The B chain folds into two topologically similar domains, each binding lactose in a shallow cleft. This finding is in agreement with results from sequencing studies, which have shown that the B chain is a gene duplication product, exhibiting about 32% amino acid identity between its amino-terminal and carboxyl-terminal halves (residues 1–135 and 136–267, respectively). In each carbohydrate binding site a glutamine residue forms a hydrogen bond with the hydroxyl at C-4 of galactose, accounting for the specificity of the lectin for this sugar and its inability to interact with glucose, which differs from galactose only in the configuration around C-4 (Fig. 5.1).

7.4 INFLUENZA VIRUS HAEMAGGLUTININ

Considerable information is available about the three dimensional structure of the influenza virus haemagglutinin and the relationship of its structure to specificity [14, 51]. As demonstrated with the haemagglutinin of a 1968 strain of influenza virus, the subunit of this lectin is composed of two chains, HA_1 (MW 36 334 Da) and HA_2 (MW 25750 Da) covalently linked by a disulphide bond. The subunits thus formed are associated non-covalently to form trimers which are located on the surface of the viral membrane. Each subunit consists of a globular domain on top of an elongated stem, projecting 135 Å from the membrane (Fig. 7.4). The globular domain is made up of HA_1 only and contains the carbohydrate binding site of the lectin. This site has the form of a pocket and is composed of amino acids that are

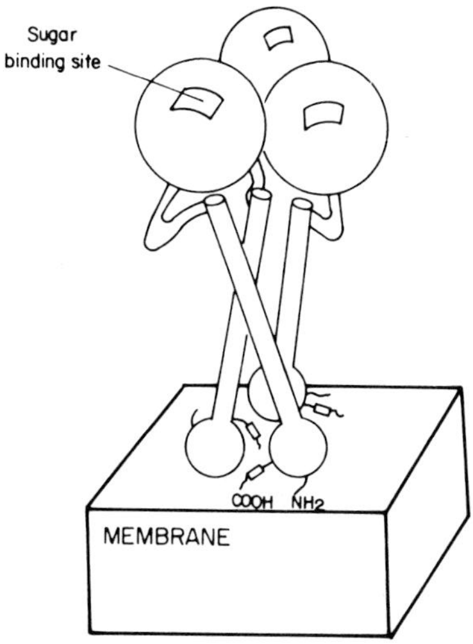
Sugar
binding site
COOH
NH2
MEMBRANE

Fig. 7.4 Schematic representation of the three dimensional structure of the influenza virus haemagglutinin. (Modified from Wilson, I.A., Skehel, J.J. and Wiley, D.C. (1981) *Nature*, **289**, 366–73.)

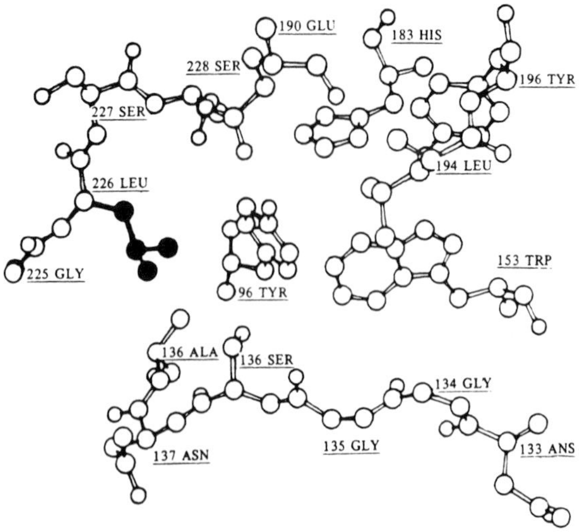
190 GLU
183 HIS
228 SER
196 TYR
227 SER
194 LEU
226 LEU
153 TRP
225 GLY
96 TYR
136 ALA
136 SER
134 GLY
137 ASN
135 GLY
133 ANS

Fig. 7.5 Selected amino acids surrounding the sialic acid binding site of the influenza virus haemagglutinin. (Reproduced with permission from Rogers, G.N., *et al.* (1983) *Nature*, **304**, 76–8.)

largely conserved in the numerous strains of the virus (Fig. 7.5). Other conserved residues are found behind the pocket and seem to stabilize the architecture of the site without being in a position to interact with the carbohydrate. By contrast, the perimeter of the pocket is composed of amino acid residues which vary during the antigenic changes that accompany recurrent epidemics for which influenza viruses are renowned.

Comparison of the haemagglutinins of five mutants of the virus with those of the parental strains showed that the mutant haemagglutinins had a lower affinity for the $\alpha 2 \rightarrow 6$ linked *N*-acetylneuraminic acid, a markedly increased affinity for the $\alpha 2 \rightarrow 3$ linked sugar, and differed from the parental strain haemagglutinins by a single amino acid substitution: leucine 226 was substituted by glutamine in four of the mutant haemagglutinins and by methionine in one of them. Crystallographic studies of complexes of the haemagglutinin of the wild type 1968 influenza virus with *N*-acetylneuraminyl $\alpha 2 \rightarrow 6$ lactose (NeuAcα2 $\rightarrow$ 6Galβ4Glc) and of one of the mutant haemagglutinins with *N*-acetylneuraminyl $\alpha 2 \rightarrow 3$ lactose (NeuAcα2 $\rightarrow$ 3Galβ4Glc) are currently in progress. Such studies are expected to reveal how a single amino acid substitution can affect the sugar specificity of a lectin.

In the crystals mentioned above, the *N*-acetylneuraminic acid of the bound *N*-acetylneuraminyllactose is fixed in the binding site, whereas the lactose is outside the site. This is consistent with affinity measurements showing that tri- and tetrasaccharides containing terminal $\alpha 2 \rightarrow 3$-linked *N*-acetylneuraminic acid have nearly the same affinity for the haemagglutinin as the methyl α-glycoside of this sugar. Thus, the binding site of the viral lectin is small and can accommodate only one α-linked monosaccharide.

CHAPTER 8
Biosynthesis

During the last decade, considerable knowledge has become available about the biosynthesis and molecular genetics of lectins, based on studies with tissue slices and cell free systems, as well as the application of recombinant DNA techniques. As with most proteins, the information for lectin synthesis, encoded in the genes and transmitted by mRNA, is utilized by the ribosomes to form precursor polypeptides in the endoplasmic reticulum. These precursors undergo co- and post-translational modifications, to form the mature lectins. A co-translational processing step common to almost all lectins is the proteolytic removal of a 20–30 amino acid signal sequence from the amino-terminal end. Most lectins also undergo co-translational *N*-glycosylation and further post-translational modifications of the carbohydrate units; *O*-glycosylation of hydroxyproline is most likely post-translational. Frequently, post-translational proteolytic cleavages occur as well. For example, the primary translation product of the fava bean lectin mRNA is a polypeptide of M_r 29 000. In this polypeptide, the NH_2-terminal signal sequence of 29 residues is followed by the β chain, and then the α chain. The lectin is thus synthesized as a single polypetide precursor (preprolectin) with the structure NH_2—signal—β chain—α chain—COOH. Pea lectin, too, is synthesized as a preprolectin of M_r 25 000 with the same orientation as that of fava bean lectin (Fig. 8.1). Removal of the signal sequence occurs in the endoplasmic reticulum and the product is then transported to the protein bodies where it is cleaved post-translationally to yield the β and α chains of the mature fava bean or pea lectin. These findings provide convincing evidence for the hypothesis, formulated originally on the basis of the sequence homologies between the two chain and single chain legume lectins, that the former are derived from a single polypeptide precursor.

The biosynthetic studies have also provided an answer to the puzzling question of the origin of the circular homology between concanavalin A and other legume lectins (Fig. 6.6). For a time it was believed that this unusual homology is a result of reorganization within a common ancestor gene, possibly involving gene duplication. However, once the cDNA encoding concanavalin A was prepared and sequenced [52], the surprising discovery was made that the amino acid sequence deduced from the cDNA sequence had a direct, linear homology (not a circular one)

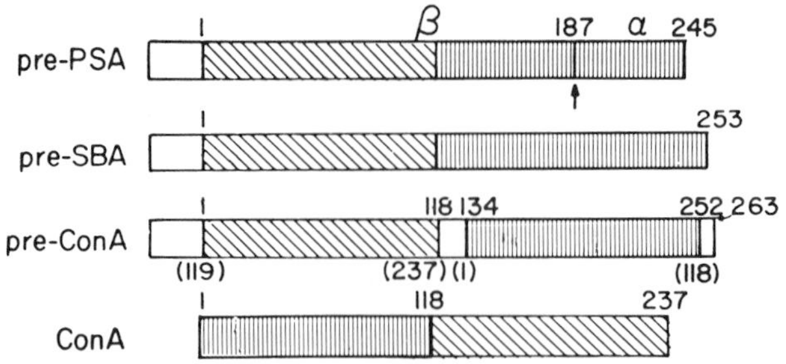
pre-PSA
1
β
187
α
245
pre-SBA
1
253
pre-ConA
1
118 134
252 263
(119)
(237) (1)
(118)
ConA
1
118
237

Fig. 8.1 Schematic structures of the precursors of pea lectin (pre-PSA), soybean agglutinin (pre-SBA) and concanavalin A (pre-ConA) and of mature concanavalin A (ConA). Arrow denotes position of cleavage into α and β chains of pea lectin; numbers in parentheses in pre-ConA give the corresponding positions in mature concanavalin A.

with the other legume lectins. The cDNA contained a region corresponding to 29 residues of a signal sequence, followed by a coding region corresponding to amino acids 119–237 of concanavalin A, a region encoding 15 amino acids not found in the mature lectin, and finally a region corresponding to amino acids 1–118 of the lectin, followed by a carboxy-terminal extension of nine residues (Fig. 8.1). Studies on the formation of concanavalin A during embryogenesis of *Canavalia ensiformis*, and on post-translational processing of the lectin, have revealed another most unusual feature [53, 54]. Although concanavalin A is not a glycoprotein, it is synthesized as a glycosylated precursor with the same amino acid sequence as that deduced from the cDNA sequence. The carbohydrate of the precursor is first removed, and then the precursor is cleaved into two polypeptides. These are then covalently linked to form a polypeptide in which the alignment of residues 1–118 and 119–237 is reversed from that of the precursor. It should be noted that the new covalent bond is between amino acids 118 and 119 in the numbering of mature concanavalin A, i.e. the cleavage position in the naturally occurring fragmented subunits of concanavalin A. The biosynthetic pathway described represents a novel means of assembling a mature protein, involving the rearrangement of a primary sequence by the removal of a C-terminal peptide and concomitant formation of a peptide bond in a reaction known as transpeptidation.

Both the deglycosylation of the concanavalin A precursor and the subsequent processing steps presumably occur after the protein has folded into a conformation very similar to that of the mature lectin (Fig. 8.2). In this conformation the region containing amino acids 118 and 119 protrudes from the main body of the subunit. Ligation of these residues with the concomitant release of the C-terminal peptide of the precursor (residues 252–263 in pre-ConA, Fig. 8.1) can thus take place with only minimal changes in the three dimensional structure of the molecule.

Another lectin which has been studied to a considerable extent with respect to its biosynthesis is *Phaseolus vulgaris* (PHA). The E and L subunits of this lectin are encoded by two genes located on the same chromosome, 4 kilobase apart, containing regions coding for signal peptides of 21 and 20 amino acids, respectively.

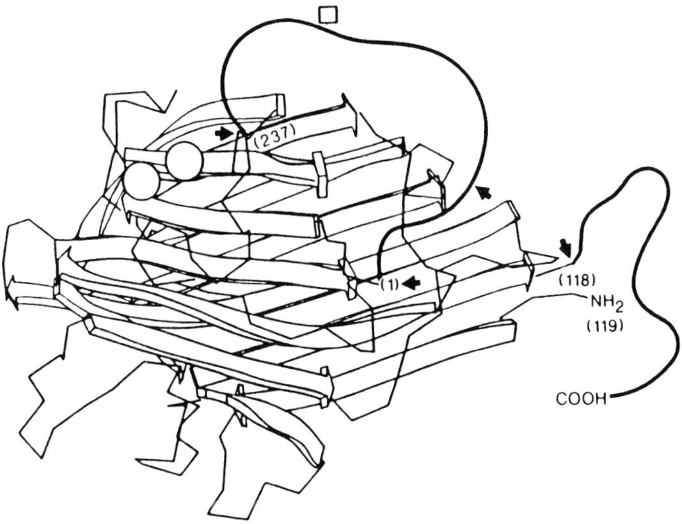
(237)
(1)
(118)
NH2
(119)
COOH

Fig. 8.2 Hypothetical three dimensional structure of the precursor of concanavalin A fitted with a computer model of the mature lectin. Numbers correspond to residue positions in mature concanavalin A. Arrows indicate the approximate positions of proteolytic processing. The proposed location of the oligosaccharide side chain is also marked. (Reproduced with permission from Bowles, D.J., Marcus, S.E., Pappin, *et al.* (1986) *J. Cell Biol.*, **102**, 1284–97, Rockefeller University Press.)

There is a high degree of homology between the mRNA coding regions of the two genes, suggesting that they are derived from the duplication of an ancestral gene.

In addition to *Phaseolus vulgaris*, several other legumes have been found to contain multiple lectin genes. These include soybean, jack bean and *Dolichos biflorus*. Of the two related lectin genes found in soybean, the L1 gene codes for the seed lectin whereas the function of the L2 gene, which is expressed at only low levels, is unknown. Both genes are also present in a lectin deficient soybean line; in this case, however, the L1 gene contains a large (3.4 kilobase) insertion within its coding region which blocks its transcription. In the cotyledons of *Phaseolus vulgaris*, soybean and pea, mRNA transcripts hybridizing with the respective lectin cDNA(s) begin to accumulate during mid-maturation and then decrease during late maturation. The increase in mRNA coincides with the period of maximal production of the seed lectins and indicates that lectin accumulation in the seeds is regulated at the transcriptional level.

In view of the close structural similarity between ricin and the *Ricinus communis* agglutinin it has been suggested that a precursor–product relationship may exist between them. That this is not the case was demonstrated by cloning experiments, which showed that the two lectins are products of distinct genes. Both are synthesized as preproproteins with a 24 amino acid *N*-terminal signal sequence preceding the A chain which is joined to the B chain by a 12 amino acid linking region. The signal peptide and the linking peptide between the A and B chains are identical for both lectins. Extensive sequence homologies exist between the corresponding chains of the toxin and the agglutinin, 93% in the A chains and 84% in the B chains. Moreover, similarly to ricin, the B chain of the agglutinin exhibits internal homology between the N-terminal and C-terminal parts of the molecule. In spite of this, the functional properties of the two castor bean lectins are markedly different.

An important recent development is the expression of lectin genes in heterologous systems: pea lectin [55], L-PHA [37] and the A chain of ricin [56] in *Escherichia coli*; and soybean agglutinin and PHA in tobacco plants [57, 58]. Although the recombinant pea lectin was obtained from the bacteria as a single polypeptide chain of MW 28 000 Da (i.e. it was not processed as in the plant into α and β chains), it possessed the same haemagglutinating activity had sugar specificity as the native lectin. L-PHA synthesized in *Escherichia coli* had the same biological activities as the lectin isolated from the red kidney beans, in spite of the fact that it was not glycosylated.

CHAPTER 9
Applications

Lectins are widely used in research and clinical laboratories, and are making a mark also in medical practice. They offer many advantages, including ready availability of numerous lectins with distinct specificities as well as high stability. Even more important is the fact that their reactions with soluble substances and cells can be reversed by simple sugars. The specific interaction of a biopolymer with a lectin may be taken as evidence that the polymer contains carbohydrate. Thus, lectin binding has been widely used to demonstrate that membrane receptors for many hormones, growth factors, neurotransmitters and toxins are glycoconjugates.

With a few exceptions (e.g. the lectins from *Helix pomatia* or from *Limulus polyphemus*), lectins derived from plants are commonly used. For applications such as those based on cell agglutination or mitogenic stimulation (for example, cell separation or chromosome mapping, respectively), the lectins are used in unmodified form. For most purposes, however, lectin derivatives are required. Immobilized lectins, such as those that are covalently bound to Sepharose are a

Table 9.1 Methods for visualization of lectin binding to glycoconjugates

Lectin derivatives	*Labelling agent*	*Methods of detection*
Radioactive	^{125}I	Monitoring of radioactivity, autoradiography
Fluorescent	Fluorescein Rhodamine	Light microscopy
Enzyme-bound	Horseradish peroxidase	Visual*
Electron-dense	Colloidal gold Ferritin	Electron microscopy
Biotinylated	Biotin	Visual or electron microscopy†

*Detection requires addition of a chromophoric substrate.
†Detected with the aid of avidin labelled with, for example, horseradish peroxidase or an electron-dense agent [59].

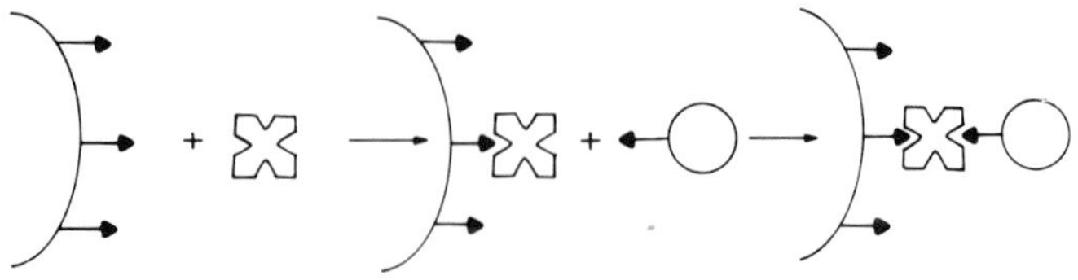
Cell surface
Lectin
Peroxidase

Fig. 9.1 Detection of cell bound lectin with horseradish peroxidase. The enzyme interacts *via* its carbohydrate chain with one of the free sugar binding sites of the lectin.

must for affinity chromatography of glycoproteins, glycopeptides and oligosaccharides. Other popular derivatives are listed in Table 9.1. Many of these were originally synthesized to allow detection of glycoconjugates in tissue sections, on cells and subcellular organelles, but are useful for other purposes as well. The derivatized lectins are applied directly to the samples to be examined. Alternatively, the preparations are treated with an unmodified lectin which is then visualized with a second reagent, for instance horseradish peroxidase or labelled anti-lectin antibodies. In the case of the peroxidase, which is a glycoprotein, an interaction takes place between the carbohydrate moieties of the enzyme and one (or more) of the unoccupied saccharide binding sites of the lectin (Fig. 9.1). This approach is therefore limited to lectins such as concanavalin A, which can bind to the carbohydrate of the peroxidase.

9.1 GLYCOCONJUGATES IN SOLUTION

9.1.1 Glycoproteins

Individual glycoproteins in complex mixtures can be readily detected with the aid of lectins. For this purpose, the glycoproteins are separated by polyacrylamide gel electrophoresis; preferably, the gels are 'blotted', i.e. the electrophoretically separated bands are transferred to a microporous membrane filter such as nitrocellulose to give a 'blot'. The glycoproteins on the blot are then revealed with the aid of lectins. For example, glycoproteins containing mannose, galactose or sialic acid (and/or *N*-acetylglucosamine) can be identified by overlaying the blots with labelled concanavalin A, peanut agglutinin (Fig. 9.2), or wheat germ agglutinin, respectively. The potential of this technique has been greatly increased since it has been demonstrated that the glycoproteins can be modified *in situ* on the blots, by treatment with glycosidases prior to the lectin overlay. This can be nicely illustrated with glycophorin, the main sialoglycoprotein of human erythrocyte membranes which contains many oligosaccharide chains terminating with *N*-acetylneuraminic acid. Blots of human erythrocyte ghost proteins are stained with wheat germ agglutinin at the position of glycophorin, whereas no staining is obtained with peanut agglutinin. After treatment of the blots with sialidase,

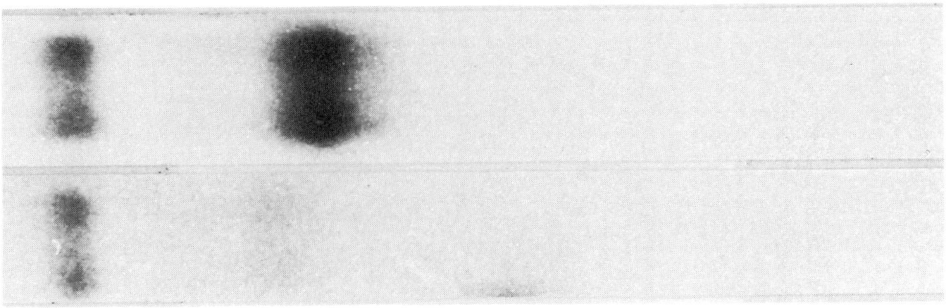

Fig. 9.2 Analysis of peanut agglutinin (PNA) receptors on mouse thymocytes by the blotting and lectin overlay technique. The plasma membranes isolated from the thymocytes were separated by polyacrylamide gel electrophoresis and the protein bands were transferred onto nitrocellulose. The right-hand lane was treated with sialidase, and the blot was overlayed with a solution of radioactively labelled peanut agglutinin. The bands which bound lectin were then revealed by autoradiography. As can be seen, the membranes contain a major PNA binding glycoprotein, MW 180 kDa. In addition, there is a band of MW 110 kDa which binds PNA only after treatment with sialidase. (Courtesy of Antonio De Maio.)

glycophorin loses its capacity to bind wheat germ agglutinin as it acquires the ability to bind peanut aglutinin.

Affinity chromatography of glycoproteins on immobilized lectins is widely employed for preparative purposes; it is also useful as an analytical technique. The solution to be fractionated is applied to a column of the immobilized lectin and the unbound materials are washed off with an appropriate solution. The specifically bound glycoproteins are then eluted with a solution of the sugar for which the lectin is specific. This procedure commonly yields a mixture of glycoproteins, but occasionally a single homogeneous one is obtained. Since lectins retain their binding activity in the presence of mild detergents, the method is extremely useful for the isolation and purification of membrane glycoproteins that require detergents for their solubilization. Many of these glycoproteins are receptors for hormones, growth factors or toxins. For instance, affinity chromatography on wheat germ agglutinin is the standard method for the partial purification of the insulin receptor from human placenta and cultured lymphocytes. The method has also been used to separate membrane vesicles with external carbohydrates from those that lack such sugars (Fig. 9.3).

The high specificity of lectins permits the resolution of even closely related compounds, such as molecular variants of a glycoprotein, that differ only slightly in their carbohydrate composition or the structure of their carbohydrate chains. This has been of great value in the investigation of glycoprotein microheterogeneity, i.e. the occurrence of variant oligosaccharides at a particular glycosylation site in different molecules of a given glycoprotein. A well studied example is ovalbumin, a major glycoprotein of hen egg white, which contains a single carbohydrate attachment site at Asn^{342}. While in any preparation of ovalbumin all molecules consist of the same polypeptide chain, the carbohydrate chains are not identical

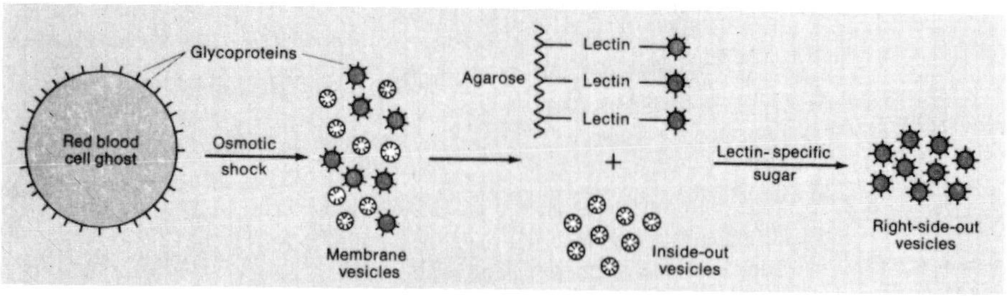
Glycoproteins
Red blood cell ghost
Osmotic shock
Membrane vesicles
Agarose
Lectin
Lectin
Lectin
+
Inside-out vesicles
Lectin-specific sugar
Right-side-out vesicles

Fig. 9.3 Separation of inside-out and right-side-out vesicles from red blood cell membranes by affinity chromatography on lectins. Vesicles prepared from red blood cell membranes (ghosts) can be either right-side-out (original external surface on the outside) or inside-out (original internal surface on the outside). The right-side-out vesicles bind to the immobilized lectin (wheat germ agglutinin), while the inside-out vesicles, because of lack of external carbohydrates, cannot bind. The lectin-bound vesicles are selectively eluted from the column with a solution of *N*-acetylglucosamine. (Reproduced with permission from Cuatrecasas, P. and Parikh, I. (1985) *Chem. Eng. News*, August 26, p. 27, copyright © 1985, American Chemical Society.)

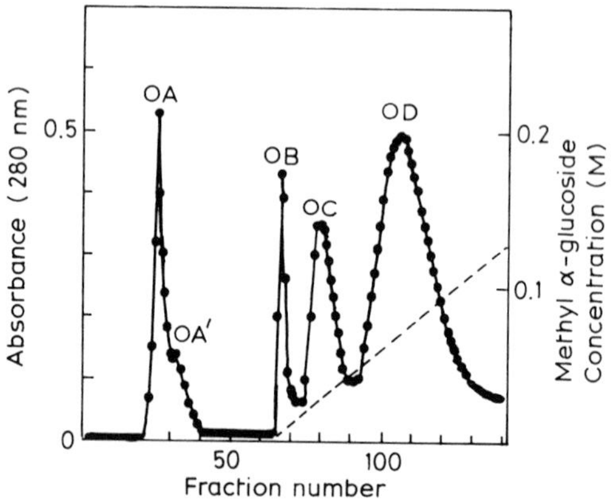
Absorbance (280 nm)
0.5
0
OA
OA′
OB
OC
OD
50
100
Fraction number
0.2
0.1
Methyl α-glucoside Concentration (M)

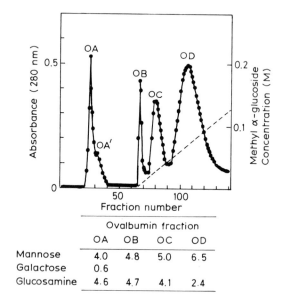

	Ovalbumin fraction			
	OA	OB	OC	OD
Mannose	4.0	4.8	5.0	6.5
Galactose	0.6			
Glucosamine	4.6	4.7	4.1	2.4

Fig.9.4 Chromatography of hen egg white albumin on concanavalin A-Sepharose. Protein (●—●); methyl α-glucoside concentration (---). The carbohydrate composition (mol/45 000 g of protein) of the peaks are shown below the figure. (Reproduced with permission from Iwase, H., Kato, Y. and Hotta, K. (1981) *J. Biol. Chem.*, **256**, 5638–42.)

even in preparations from a single egg of a pure bred chicken; indeed, about 20 different oligosaccharides have been identified in this glycoprotein. Affinity chromatography of ovalbumin on concanavalin A yielded four major subfractions that differed in their carbohydrate composition (Fig. 9.4). Further fractionation on wheat germ agglutinin afforded three subfractions that were homogeneous, in that each contained only one species of carbohydrate chain. Other purified glycoproteins were similarly separated into distinct molecular species by affinity chromatography on immobilized lectins. Two subpopulations of the mammalian β-adrenergic receptor, one containing oligomannose units and the other with complex type carbohydrates, have been obtained by affinity chromatography on concanavalin A and wheat germ agglutinin, respectively. Affinity chromatography on a series of lectin columns provided evidence that the normal glycosylation pattern of the α subunit common to all pituitary glycoprotein hormones (e.g. human chorionic gonadotropin) is altered in patients with pituitary tumours [59a]. Similar experiments with human ribonucleases revealed organ-specific differences in the structure of their carbohydrate chains.

With a battery of immobilized lectins, mixtures of glycopeptides or oligosaccharides obtained by enzymatic or chemical cleavage of purified glycoproteins can be separated into homogeneous compounds [60, 61]. This is illustrated in Fig. 9.5. The patterns of binding to, and elution from, the lectin columns also provide information on the composition, sequence, linkage and branching of oligosac-

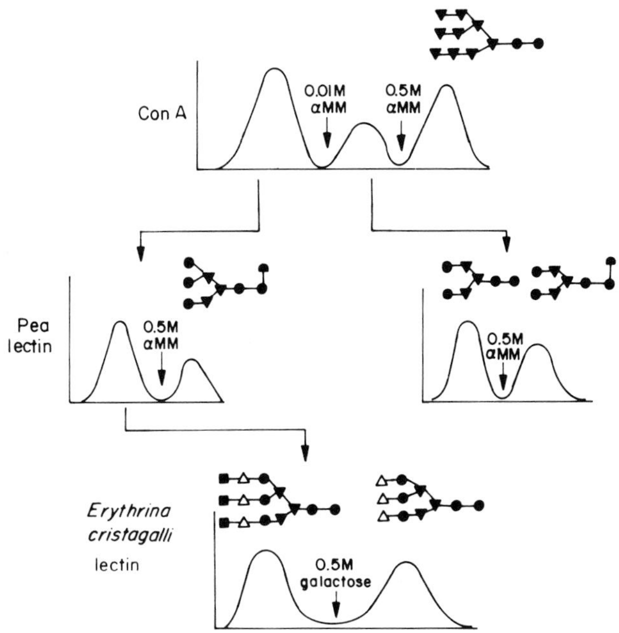
Con A
0.01M
αMM
0.5M
αMM
Pea
lectin
0.5M
αMM
0.5M
αMM
Erythrina
cristagalli
lectin
0.5M
galactose

Fig. 9.5 Scheme for fractionation of a mixture of *N*-linked oligosaccharides by sequential affinity chromatography on lectins. αMM, methyl α-mannoside.

charides and of the carbohydrate units of glycopeptides [61]. In combination with glycosidases and other chemical and physical methods (such as nuclear magnetic resonance), lectins thus serve as powerful aids for structural studies of complex carbohydrates.

9.1.2 Glycolipids

In contrast to the widespread use of lectins for the detection, isolation and structural studies of glycoproteins, their application to the investigation of glycolipids has until recently been limited. This was largely due to the lack of suitable methods for the examination of the interactions of glycolipids with lectins. The situation changed with the introduction, in 1980, of the solid phase autoradiographic ('overlay') technique for the detection of glycosphingolipids on thin layer plates after chromatography [62]. Developed originally to reveal the interaction of glycosphingolipids with toxins and antibodies, it was soon adapted to lectins as well. In this method, glycolipids separated by thin layer chromatography are revealed directly on the plates with the aid of a derivatized lectin (cf. Table 9.1). Similarly to glycoproteins on blots, glycolipids can be modified enzymatically *in situ* on the thin layer chromatograms prior to the lectin overlay.

Soybean agglutinin, which binds preferentially to globoside and trihexosyl ceramide (Table 9.2), has been utilized to examine glycosphingolipids from bovine erythrocytes and to reveal differences in the surface glycolipids of cultured adrenergic and cholinergic neurons. The lectin from *Helix pomatia* does not bind to neutral glycosphingolipids from human B and O type erythrocytes, but binds to five components in lipid extracts from A and AB type cells. This is in agreement with the A blood group specificity of the lectin and confirms the polymorphism of blood group active glycolipids. *Erythrina cristagalli* agglutinin, specific for N-acetyllactosamine, binds preferentially to *para*-globoside (which contains N-acetyllactosamine at its non-reducing end, see Table 9.2) and is thus suitable for the detection of small amounts of this glycolipid in biological materials such as extracts of erythrocyte membranes and of granulocytes (Fig. 9.6) [63].

Table 9.2 Structures of neutral glycosphingolipids

Name	*Structure*
Lactosylceramide	Galβ4Glcβ1Cer
Trihexosylceramide	Galα4Galβ4Glcβ1Cer
Globoside	GalNAcβ3Galα4Galβ4Glcβ1Cer
para-Globoside	Galβ4GlcNAcβ3Galβ4Glcβ1Cer
Asialo-G_{M1}	Galβ3GalNAcβ4Galβ4Glcβ1Cer
Forsmann antigen	GalNAcα3GalNAcβ3Galα4Galβ4Glcβ1Cer
Pentahexosylceramide	Galα3Galβ4GlcNAcβ3Galβ4Glcβ1Cer

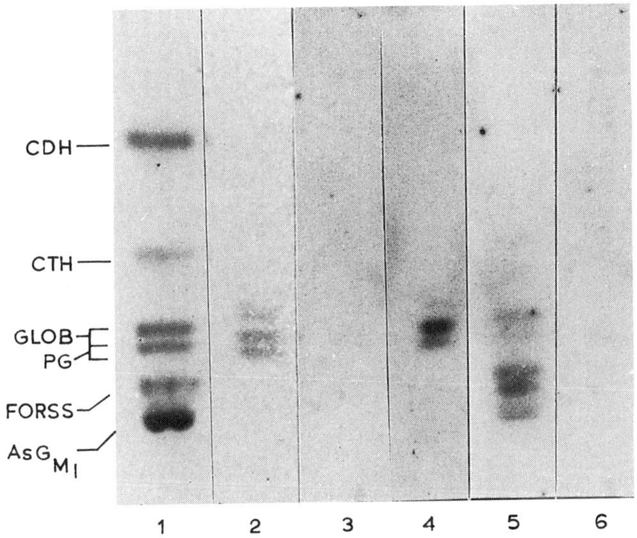
CDH
CTH
GLOB
PG
FORSS
AsG_{M1}
1
2
3
4
5
6

Fig. 9.6 Binding of ^{125}I-labeled lectins from *Erythrina cristagalli* and from soybean glycosphingolipids after HPTLC. Lanes 1, 3, 5: standard mixture containing lactosylceramide (CDH), trihexosylceramide (CTH), globoside (GLOB), Forssman antigen (FORSS) and asialo-GM_1 (AsG_{M1}); lanes 2, 4, 6: *para*-globoside (PG). Lanes 1, 2: staining with orcinol; lanes 3, 4: autoradiogram of overlays with *Erythrina cristagalli* agglutinin and lanes 5, 6 with soybean agglutinin. (Reproduced with permission from Ehrlich-Rogozinski, S., De Maio, A., Lis, H. and Sharon, N. (1987) *Glycoconjugate J.*, **4**, 379–90.)

9.1.3 Other carbohydrate derivatives

Other classes of carbohydrate containing compounds have been fractionated with the aid of lectins, as shown by the following examples. Affinity chromatography on a column of *Griffonia simplicifolia* lectin I was used to separate UDP-GalNAc from UDP-GlcNAc in the assay UDP-GlcNAc-4-epimerase (the enzyme catalysing the interconversion of the two sugar nucleotides). The method is also useful for the preparation of UDP-GalNAc from the more readily available UDP-GlcNAc. Separation of these two sugar nucleotides has been achieved by high performance liquid chromatography on a *Ricinus communis* agglutinin column [64].

Affinity chromatography on lectins greatly facilitates the assay of UDP-GlcNAc transferase V, the enzyme that transfers *N*-acetyglucosamine from UDP-GlcNAc to the α6-linked mannose of the dibranched oligosaccharide GlcNAcβ2Manα6(GlcNAcβ2Manα3)Manβ to give the tribranched saccharide GlcNAcβ2(GlcNAcβ6)Manα6(GlcNAcβ2Manα3)Manβ (Fig. 9.7). Taking advantage of the fact that the dibranched substrate, but not the tribranched product, binds to concanavalin A, the unreacted substrate is removed from the incubation mixture by chromatography on this lectin. The product is then obtained in pure

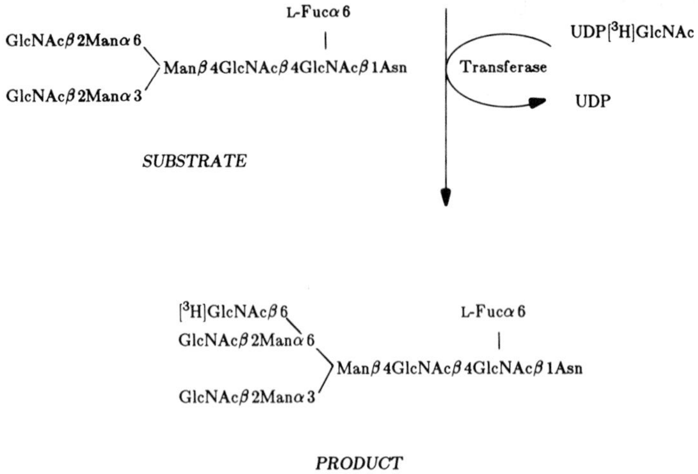
L-Fucα6
GlcNAcβ2Manα6
Manβ4GlcNAcβ4GlcNAcβ1Asn
GlcNAcβ2Manα3
SUBSTRATE
UDP[³H]GlcNAc
Transferase
UDP
[³H]GlcNAcβ6
GlcNAcβ2Manα6
L-Fucα6
Manβ4GlcNAcβ4GlcNAcβ1Asn
GlcNAcβ2Manα3
PRODUCT

Fig. 9.7 Affinity chromatography on lectins in the assay of UDP-GlcNAc transferase V activity. The unreacted substrate is removed from the reaction mixture by adsorption to concanavalin A and the product is isolated in pure form by binding to, and elution from, immobilized lentil lectin.

form, separated from the unreacted sugar donor, and from UDP by binding to, and elution from, immobilized lentil lectin [65].

An unconventional application of lectins is for the isolation of tRNA species containing bases glycosylated with either mannose or galactose. The mannose containing $tRNA^{Asp}$ from rabbit liver, rat liver and rat ascites hepatoma was isolated on a column of concanavalin A–Sepharose, and the galactose containing $tRNA^{Tyr}$ from the same sources was purified by affinity chromatography on a column of *Ricinus communis* agglutinin–Sepharose.

9.2 MEMBRANE BOUND SUGARS

Prior to the introduction of lectins into histo- and cytochemistry, there were only general reagents for the detection of sugars in cells and tissues. Thanks to the availability of lectins it is possible to visualize specific sugar residues and sequences, and to obtain more information on the location and structure of particular glycoconjugates. Lectins are, therefore, increasingly employed in cytological investigations of membrane structure, of intracelluar pathways of protein glycosylation and of changes that occur in glycoconjugates during differentiation, growth and development. Since modifications in content, distribution and accessibility of cellular and extracellular glycoconjugates are often associated with pathological processes, it is not surprising that much effort is being invested in screening lectins for their potential as diagnostic reagents in clinical situations.

9.2.1 Cell surfaces

Both on intact cells and isolated plasma membranes, lectins bind exclusively to the outer surface. This finding was among the very first demonstrations that carbohydrates are asymmetrically distributed on membranes. Lectins were among the probes initially used to demonstrate the fluid character of biological membranes and to investigate the movement of membrane constituents to form clusters and caps (Fig. 9.8). Furthermore, following initial cell surface binding, the fate of endocytosed plasma membrane fragments could be traced in different cell types, e.g. neurons.

Quantitative and qualitative changes in lectin binding have been observed in the course of cell division, maturation and differentiation, as well as other cellular events, in a variety of cells and tissues. For example, receptors for *Dolichos biflorus* agglutinin are selectively expressed on mouse foetal thymocytes, but are absent on adult thymocytes and most other tissues of the mouse. The lectins of peanut, *Lotus tetragonolobus, Dolichos biflorus* and *Erythrina cristagalli* bind to embryonal carcinoma cells (which are stem cells of teratocarcinoma and resemble in many respects multi-potential cells of early embryos), but not to their differentiated derivatives. On pre-implantation mouse embryos, *Dolichos biflorus* lectin binds extensively only to blastomers of 2- and 4-cell stage.

Examination of tissue sections provides information on cellular and regional patterns of lectin binding in organs such as kidney, muscle, retina and pancreas, as well as on their developmental stage. For instance, in sections of epidermis of the newborn rat, *Griffonia simplicifolia* lectin IB_4 binds preferentially to the basal (innermost) cells (Fig. 9.9). The binding is primarily to α-linked galactose residues of laminin, a major non-collagenous glycoprotein constituent of basal membranes. As the cells differentiate and move through two intermediate layers of the epidermis towards the outer cornified layer, binding of the lectin decreases progressively. *Ulex europaeus* lectin I, on the other hand, binds strongly to cells of the intermediate layers but not to those of the basal and cornified layers. Studies of the effect of

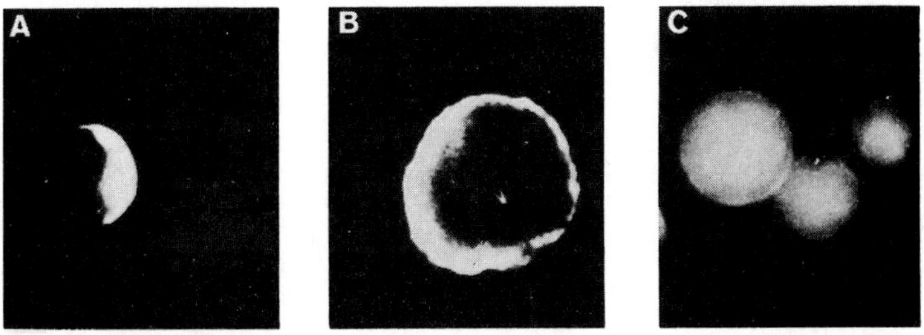
A
B
C

Fig. 9.8 Binding of fluorescein labeled concanavalin A to cells. A, Normal rat lymphocytes; B, mouse lymphoma cells; C, lymphocytes fixed with glutaraldehyde prior to addition of fluorescein–concanavalin A. (Reproduced with permission from Inbar, M. and Sachs, L. (1973) *FEBS Lett.*, **32**, 124–8.)

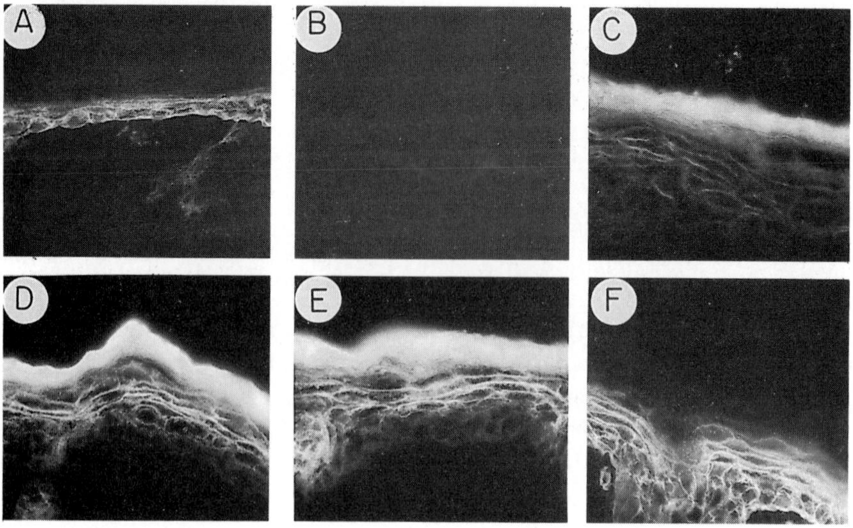
A
B
C
D
E
F

Fig. 9.9 Photomicrograph of skin sections treated with fluoresceinated *Griffonia simplicifolia* lectin IB_4 (A, B, C) and fluoresceinated *Ulex europaeus* agglutinin I (D, E, F); (A, D) unmodified specimens; (B, E) sections pretreated with α-galactosidase; (C, F) sections pretreated with α-fucosidase. (Reproduced with permission from Zieske, J.D. and Bernstein, I.A. (1982) *J. Cell Biol.*, **95**, 626–31, Rockefeller University Press.)

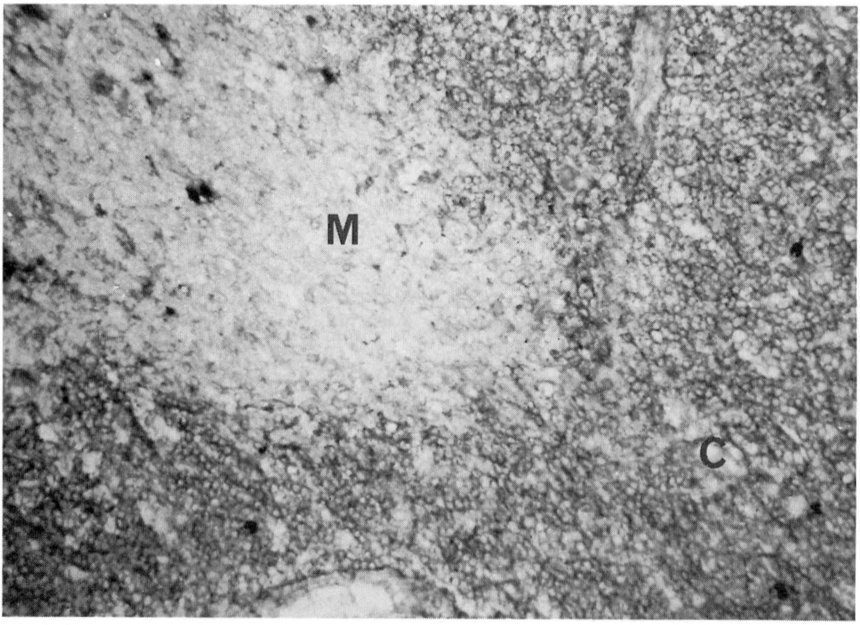
M
C

Fig. 9.10 Binding of horseradish peroxidase–peanut agglutinin to mouse thymus. C, cortex; M, medulla. (Reproduced with permission from Rose, M.L. and Malchiodi, F. (1981) *Immunology*, **42**, 583–91.)

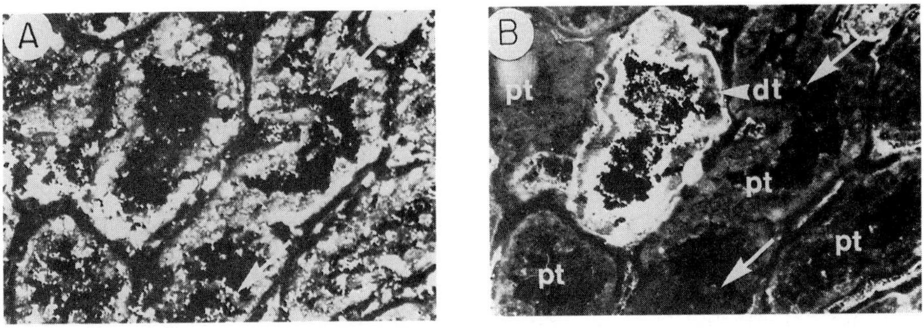
A
B
pt
dt
pt
pt
pt

Fig.9.11 Binding of rhodamine labelled purified *Escherichia coli* type P fimbriae (A) and of fluorescein labelled peanut agglutinin (B) to frozen sections of human kidney. The fimbriae bind to proximal (pt; arrows) and distal (dt) tubules, while peanut agglutinin binds only to the distal tubules. (Reproduced with permission from Korhonen, T.K., Virkola, R. and Holthöfer, H. (1986) *Infect. Immun.*, 54, 328–32.)

glycosidases on the interaction of the two lectins with the different cell layers have led to the suggestion that the shift in binding from *Griffonia simplicifolia* IB_4 lectin to *Ulex europaeus* I lectin as the cells differentiate is the result of the addition of L-fucose residues to cell surface glycoconjugates that mask the receptors for the former lectin.

There are several examples of differences in lectin binding to distinct domains within an organ which can be functionally correlated. Both in mouse and human thymus, peanut agglutinin stains almost exclusively the thymic cortex, where the immunologically immature cells reside (Fig. 9.10), and does not stain the medulla regions where the mature cells are located. A more recent example involves the use of type P fimbriae, a bacterial lectin specific for Galα4Gal, characteristic of strains of *E. coli* causing urinary tract infections. Binding of the purified fimbriae to frozen sections of human kidney was predominantly to epithelial elements such as cytoplasmic sites of collecting ducts and of distal and proximal tubules (Fig. 9.11). Since fimbriae mediate the attachment of the bacteria to host tissues in the initial stage of infection, the pattern observed is indicative of a natural route of bacterial invasion leading to the glomeruli [66].

9.2.2 Subcellular organelles

As with outer cell membranes, binding studies with lectins provided evidence for the presence of carbohydrates on intracellular membranes. Here, too, carbohydrate distribution was found to be asymmetric. The carbohydrates are located on the noncytoplasmic (lumenal) surface of subcellular organelles such as mitochondria, rough microsomes and Golgi apparatus. They are also present on the membranes that constitute the nuclear envelope.

Experiments with lectins helped to localize the intracellular sites of protein glycosylation. Although the sequence of reactions leading to the formation of $Glc_3Man_9GlcNAc_2$-PP-Dol, which serves as the carbohydrate donor of

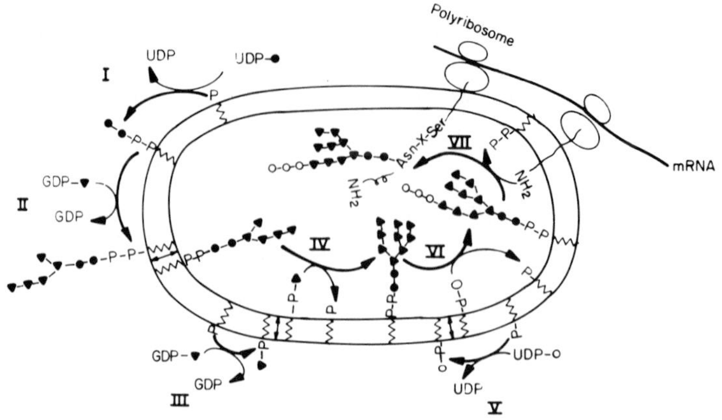
Polyribosome
UDP
UDP
I
P
mRNA
VII
Asn-X-Ser
NH2
GDP
II
GDP
IV
VI
GDP
GDP
III
UDP-o
UDP
V

Fig. 9.12 Model for the topography of glycosylation in the rough endoplasmic reticulum. ~~~~, dolichol; P, phosphate. (Modified with permission from Hirschberg, C.B. and Snider, M.D. (1987) *Ann. Rev. Biochem.*, 56, 63–87.)

N-glycosylation, has been known for some time, the subcellular sites of the individual reactions are still not completely worked out. Using concanavalin A it was found that the lipid linked oligosaccharides Man_{3-5} $GlcNAc_2$ are located on the cytoplasmic side of microsomes from cultured fibroblasts, while the lipid linked $Man_{6-9}GlcNAc_2$ and $Glc_{1-3}Man_9GlcNAc_2$ are facing the lumen of the endoplasmic reticulum. The $Man_5GlcNAc_2$-lipid seems, therefore, to be assembled on the cytoplasmic side of the endoplasmic reticulum membrane and then translocated to the lumenal side, where it is converted to $Glc_3Man_9GlcNAc_2$-lipid.

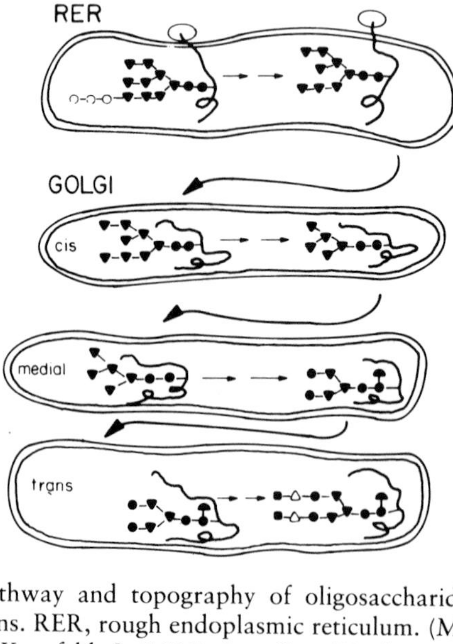
RER
GOLGI
cis
medial
trans

Fig. 9.13 Schematic pathway and topography of oligosaccharide processing on newly synthesized glycoproteins. RER, rough endoplasmic reticulum. (Modified with permission from Kornfeld, R. and Kornfeld, S. (1985) *Ann. Rev. Biochem.*, 54, 631–64.)

Using cells of mice and rats and a panel of lectins with different sugar specificities, a staining pattern has been obtained that supports the conclusions, based on the use of other methods, regarding the subcellular location of the reactions involved in the processing (or maturation) of *N*-glycosyl units of glycoproteins (Fig. 9.12). Thus, mannose specific lectins, for instance concanavalin A, bind mainly to the endoplasmic reticulum, as well as to the proximal (*cis*) cisternae of the Golgi apparatus, where the *N*-linked units are largely in their oligomannose form; lectins specific for saccharides that are found on the outer branches of *N*-acetyllactosamine type chains (e.g. wheat germ agglutinin and the *Ricinus communis* agglutinin) bind exclusively to the distal (*trans*) cisternae of the Golgi stack where the attachment of *N*-acetyglucosamine and galactose to the *N*-linked units occurs (Fig. 9.13).

9.2.3 In malignancy and metastasis

Numerous studies have been carried out on the extent and pattern of lectin binding to malignant cells compared with normal ones. Such investigations have contributed to our knowledge of the structural changes in cell surface saccharides that accompany malignant transformation, as well as those that characterize the process of metastasis. They also raised the possibility that lectin receptors may prove to be discriminating markers for neoplastic cells and tissues.

Although the number of examples of differences in the binding of lectins to malignant cells, compared with their normal counterparts, is steadily increasing, the clinical value of such findings is limited. The main reason for this is that tumours generally show extensive cellular heterogeneity, so that there are considerable variations in lectin binding observed not only with cells from different patients with the same type of malignancy, but also with cells from the same patient. A diagnostically useful lectin is *Ulex europaeus* agglutinin I which is considered to be a reliable marker for endothelial cells and tumours of vascular origin. Another lectin which promises to become clinically useful is that from *Helix pomatia*. It appears to recognize a marker of breast cancer associated with both high metastatic potential and aggressive tumour behaviour in young women. Based on a long range study that lasted for almost 20 years, in which binding of the lectin to breast tissue of close to 200 patients was examined, it was concluded that *Helix pomatia* agglutinin may be of value in assessing long term prognosis of breast cancer recurrence or survival (Fig. 9.14). There are also numerous reports indicating that reactivity with peanut agglutinin may be of help in detecting several human carcinomas, mainly those of breast, colon and lung [67].

Differences between cell surface glycoproteins on tumour cell sublines of low or high metastatic potential have been detected by the use of lectins. Certain poorly metastatic B16 melanoma sublines bind less concanavalin A than highly metastatic ones, while the latter possess fewer binding sites for soybean and wheat germ agglutinins. The metastatic capacity of murine tumour cell lines appears to be influenced by the degree of sialylation of specific membrane glycoconjugates detectable with lectins. Binding sites for the lectins from soybean, *Vicia villosa* and

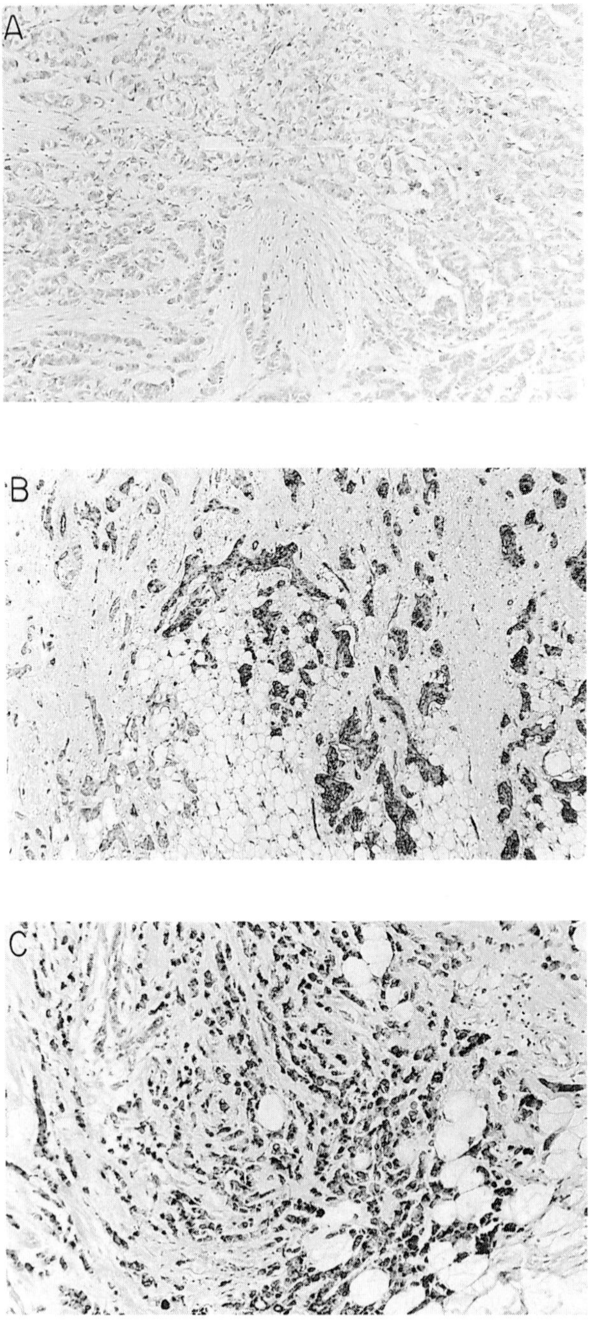
A
B
C

Fig. 9.14 Breast cancer sections stained with *Helix pomatia* agglutinin and haematoxylin, showing no staining (A), moderate staining (B) and strong staining (C). Patient A had no axillary node metastases or other recurrences; her survival was long. Patients B and C had axillary node metastases and short survival. (Reproduced with permission from Leathem, A.J. and Brooks, S.A. (1987) *Lancet*, **i**, 1054–6.)

Helix pomatia are expressed on cells of a mouse lymphoma line with low metastatic potential, but are blocked by sialic acid on cells of a high metastatic variant of the same line. Conversely, binding sites for peanut agglutinin were more sialylated on the low metastatic tumour line than on the high metastatic one. A non-metastatic revertant of the metastatic variant again bound large amounts of soybean agglutinin. (For further studies on the correlation between surface carbohydrates and metastatic potential of malignant cells see Chapter 10).

9.2.4 Other pathological states

Lysosomal storage diseases are characterized by deficiencies in specific hydrolases which catabolize tissue constituents, primarily glycoconjugates. As a result, cells accumulate the corresponding substrates in their lysosomes. In a number of cases, this accumulation could be revealed by lectin staining [68, 69]. For instance, neurons, as well as other cell types of patients with fucosidosis, a disease characterized by deficiency in α-L-fucosidase, are stained intensely with *Ulex europaeus* agglutinin I, whereas normal cells are not. Material stored in cells from patients with I cell disease, in which several glycosidases are defective, binds concanavalin A and wheat germ agglutinin, whereas cells of patients with mannosidosis (caused by deficiency of α-mannosidase) are stained intensely only with concanavalin A.

Pneumocytes (lung cells) do not stain with peanut agglutinin unless treated with

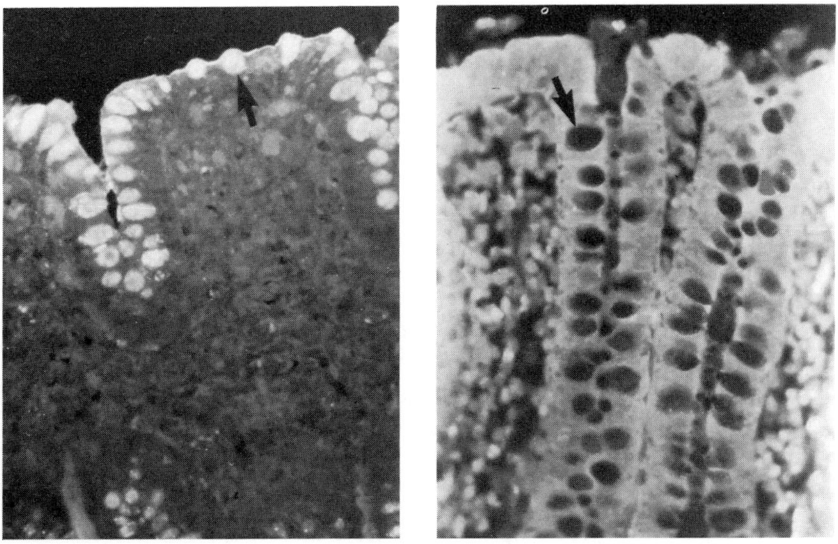

Fig. 9.15 Human colonic mucosa stained with *Dolichos biflorus* agglutinin. Colonic mucosal biopsy from patient with ischemic colitis (left) and from patient with Crohn's colitis (right). (Reproduced with permission from Jacobs, L.R. and Huber, P.W. (1985) *J. Clin. Invest.*, 75, 112–8, Copyright © Rockefeller University Press.)

sialidase; pneumocytes from patients with pneumonia, on the other hand, stain abnormally with the lectin, presumably because of the action of a pneumococcal sialidase which unmasks the galactose to which peanut agglutinin binds [70].

Parathyroid cells do not normally bind peanut agglutinin or *Ulex europaeus* agglutinin I. However, in glands that have undergone pathological changes, e.g. atrophy due to a hyperfunctioning parathyroid adenoma, many cells react with these two lectins. With the aid of *Ulex europaeus* agglutinin I and *Dolichos biflorus* agglutinin, inflammation related changes in the distribution of glycoconjugates have been found in the large intestine. For example, in Crohn's disease (an inflammatory bowel disease) a loss of L-fucose and of *N*-acetylgalactosamine were observed in the left and descending colon, respectively (Fig. 9.15). Abnormal binding of peanut agglutinin to colonic epithelium was seen in ulcerative colitis. Interestingly, these abnormal patterns of glycosylation, noted also in cancer of the colon, occur normally in the foetal intestine.

9.3 MAPPING NEURONAL PATHWAYS

A recent and rapidly growing application of lectins is in neuroanatomy as tracers for mapping neuronal connections [71]. The method is based on the injection *in vivo* of the lectin into a specified site in the nervous system, such as the region of selected neural terminals in the brain. The lectin is then taken up by the neurons and transported from the axonal termini to the nerve cell (retrograde transport) or forward to the axonal target areas (anterograde transport). To enable

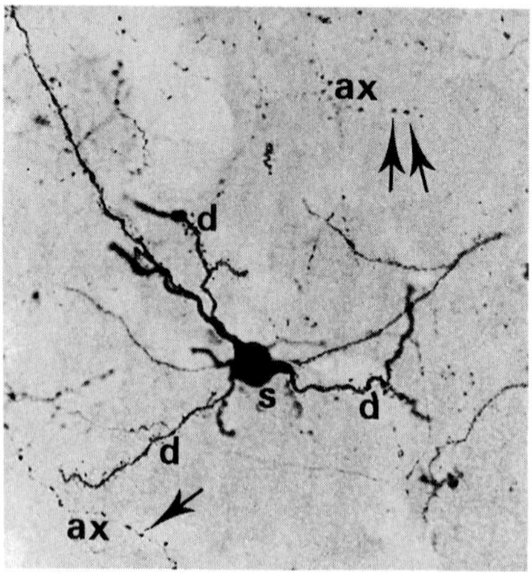
ax
d
s
d
d
ax

Fig. 9.16 Photomicrograph of a neuron labeled with L-PHA. The picture displays the soma (s) and the entire extent of the dentritic trees (d). Around the neuron, several thin axons (ax) are visible. (Reproduced with permission from Wouterlood, F.G. and Groenewegen, H.J. (1985) *Brain Res.*, **326**, 188–91.)

its detection in the nervous system, the lectin is labelled either with horseradish peroxidase or with a radioactive marker.

Radioactively iodinated wheat germ agglutinin was the first lectin to be used as a tracer in neuroanatomical studies and is now the most popular reagent for this purpose. Other lectins have more recently come into use, especially PHA. Both wheat germ agglutinin and PHA are considered to be superior tracers, in that they are taken up very efficiently and do not readily diffuse away from the injection site (Fig. 9.16). The latter property is of importance since it allows injection of the lectin into small, well defined sites. For uptake to occur, the lectin must apparently bind to its receptors, since whenever it was injected together with an inhibitory sugar, the subsequent labelling of the neuronal projections was markedly diminished. When ricin conjugates were used as tracers, morphological lesions and cell death in neurons were observed. This 'suicide transport' offers a new approach for tackling neurobiological problems, for example by denervating target organs in the peripheral nervous system.

9.4 CELL SEPARATION

In principle, any population of cells – whether from animals or plants, or of microorganisms – may be sorted into subpopulations with the aid of lectins, provided the subpopulations differ in their cell surface sugars. Since the binding of lectins to cells is readily reversed by the addition of an appropriate sugar, both the lectin-reactive and non-reactive cells are recovered, resulting in high yields (80% or more) of undamaged, fully viable cells. In this respect, lectins offer a distinct advantage over antibodies to cell surface constituents, since it is often impossible to remove the antibodies from the cells to which they are bound.

The first application of lectins for cell separation was reported in 1949 by Li and Osgood who developed a method for the separation of leukocytes from erythrocytes in human blood with the aid of PHA. The erythrocytes were selectively agglutinated by the lectin and were removed from the mixture by centrifugation. Selective agglutination is still the most widely used technique for cell separation by lectins, although this can be achieved by other methods as well. These include affinity chromatography of cells on immobilized lectins, or the use of a fluorescence activated cell sorter (FACS), in which cells are sorted one by one, usually according to the amount of fluorescent lectin bound.

Peanut agglutinin and soybean agglutinin have proved to be particularly valuable for cell separation. The most important application of the former is for the fractionation of mouse or human thymocytes into two subpopulations, an agglutinated, peanut agglutinin positive (PNA^+) and an unagglutinated (PNA^-) one (Fig. 9.17). The PNA^+ fraction consists of immunologically immature cortical cells which represent about 85–90% of the total thymocytes. PNA^- cells (10–15% of thymocytes) correspond to mature, medullary thymocytes. Although the presence of the two cell populations in the thymus has been recognized for some

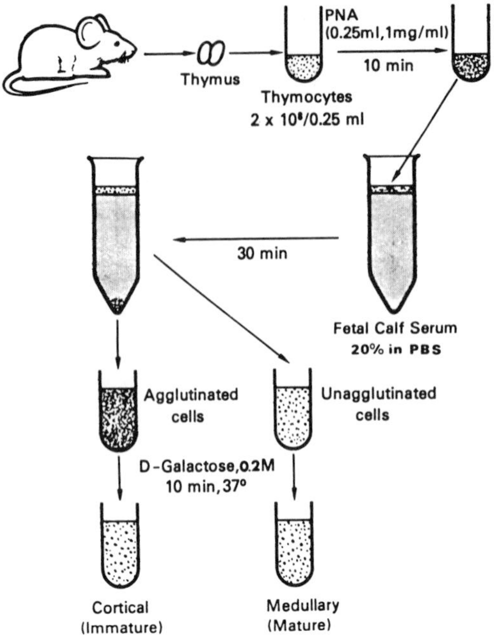
PNA
(0.25ml,1mg/ml)
10 min
Thymus
Thymocytes
2 x 10^8/0.25 ml
30 min
Fetal Calf Serum
20% in PBS
Agglutinated cells
Unagglutinated cells
D-Galactose,0.2M
10 min, 37°
Cortical
(Immature)
Medullary
(Mature)

Fig. 9.17 Fractionation of mouse thymocytes into cortical and medullary cells by peanut agglutinin.

time, separation with peanut agglutinin provided, for the first time, access to the individual thymocyte subpopulations and made it possible to examine *in vitro* the developmental and functional relationship between them. As a result, peanut agglutinin has become one of the most widely used lectins in immunological research.

Soybean agglutinin is employed for the fractionation of mouse splenocytes into B and T cells by selective agglutination of the B cells. However, the main application of this lectin is for the fractionation of human bone marrow for transplantation, as discussed in section 9.6.3. The lectin from *Erythrina cristagalli* agglutinates 85–95% of human peripheral blood mononuclear cells. The unagglutinated cell population remaining after removal of the agglutinated cells is highly enriched, both phenotypically and functionally, for natural killer cells, i.e. naturally occurring cytotoxic lymphocytes [72].

9.5 LECTINS IN MICROBIOLOGICAL STUDIES

Agglutination of bacteria from a primary isolate with a particular lectin may serve to confirm the identity of the organism, making it possible to dispense with expensive and time consuming culturing or serological testing. For example, *Bacillus anthracis*, an organism particularly difficult to identify in the clinical laboratory, can be easily confirmed by agglutination with soybean agglutinin or the lectin from *Helix pomatia*. Similarly, *Neisseria gonorrhoeae* can be identified using wheat germ agglutinin. To date, lectins have been employed as an aid for the identification of many bacterial genera, in addition to *Neisseria* and *Bacillus*. These include *Streptococcus, Staphylococcus*, and *Legionella*. As more lectins become available, their application in diagnostic microbiology will undoubtedly increase.

Fluorescein labelled lectins with different sugar specificities were used to study the composition and organization of cell walls of yeasts of various taxonomic groups. With the aid of concanavalin A, mannan was shown to be located on the outer surface of some yeasts (e.g. *Saccharomyces cerevisiae* and *Candida rugosa*) but seemed to be overlaid with other components in other yeast species (e.g. *Schizosaccharomyces*). Wheat germ agglutinin stained the cell wall as well as the cross wall of *Staphylococcus aureus*.

9.6 CLINICAL USES

9.6.1 Blood typing

The earliest clinical application of lectins was for distinguishing between erythrocytes of different blood types. Although lectins are now being superseded by blood type specific monoclonal antibodies, several are still widely used in blood banks as an aid in blood typing (Table 9.3). Thus, the lectins from *Lotus*

Table 9.3 Blood type specific lectins

Specificity	*Lectin*
Anti-A	*Griffonia simplicifolia* IA_4
	Helix pomatia (garden snail)
	Phaseolus lunatus (lima bean)
	Vicia cracca (common vetch)
Anti-A_1	*Dolichos biflorus** (horse gram)
Anti-B	*Griffonia simplicifolia* IB_4
Anti-O(H)	*Anguilla anguilla* (eel)
	Lotus tetragonolobus (asparagus pea)
	*Ulex europeus** (gorse)
Anti-A + N	*Moluccella laevis* (Irish Bell)
Anti-N	*Vicia graminea**
Anti-T	*Arachis hypogaea** (peanut)
Anti-Tn	*Salvia sclarea*

*Commonly used in blood banks.

tetragonolobus and *Ulex europaeus* are employed to identify blood type O cells, and for the identification of secretors, individuals who secrete blood group substances in their saliva and other body fluids (about 80% of the population). The lectin from *Dolichos biflorus* is used to distinguish between A_1 and A_2 subgroups, while that from *Vicia graminea* is used to differentiate between M and N cells. Occasionally lectins are employed to separate mixed erythrocyte populations, for example in the rare cases of blood group mosaicism resulting from chimerism, somatic mutation or bone marrow transplantation. Thus, as early as 1957, the *Dolichos biflorus* lectin provided conclusive evidence that a woman whose blood type was A + O was a chimera, since her A and O erythrocytes could be separated by agglutination of the former cells with the lectin.

Another application of lectins is in the differential diagnosis of 'polyagglutination' (or 'polyagglutinability'), a condition accompanying certain bacterial and viral infections, in which human erythrocytes become agglutinable by antibodies normally present in the sera of nearly all human adults. One type of polyagglutination is due to the appearance on human erythrocytes of a new antigen, known as the T antigen, which is the disaccharide galactosyl $\beta 1 \rightarrow 3$ *N*-acetylgalactosamine. In normal cells this disaccharide is masked by *N*-acetylneuraminic acid; the T antigen appears as a result of the action of the sialidase of infective bacteria or viruses. T Antigen positive erythrocytes may undergo haemolysis by the anti-T antibodies normally present in the serum, which in extreme cases leads to acute renal failure. The situation is greatly aggravated if patients carrying the polyagglutinable erythrocytes are given transfusions of fresh whole blood and plasma products. The risk to the patient can be avoided by transfusion of washed erythrocytes alone. Early detection of polyagglutination is therefore clinically important and is recommended for all patients with severe infection, unexplained haemolysis and transfusion reactions. Prior to 1963, time consuming procedures were required to detect the T antigen; with the discovery that peanut agglutinin is specific for this antigen, determination of T polyagglutination became greatly simplified. There are several case reports in the literature of patients whose lives have been saved by the use of peanut agglutinin for the early detection of polyagglutination [73].

9.6.2 Mitogenic stimulation

Mitogenic stimulation by lectins, in particular PHA and concanavalin A (for T lymphocytes) and pokeweed mitogen (for B cells), provides an easy and simple means to assess the immunocompetence of patients suffering from a diversity of diseases, recently also in cases of AIDS (Fig. 9.18). Since 1973 it has been employed to test the lymphocyte efficiency of astronauts and cosmonauts after space flights (section 9.7). Mitogenic lectins are also used to monitor the effects of various immunosuppressive and immunotherapeutic manipulations. The ability of the lymphocytes to respond to mitogens is examined by measuring either cell proliferation (e.g. stimulation of DNA synthesis) or specific immune functions,

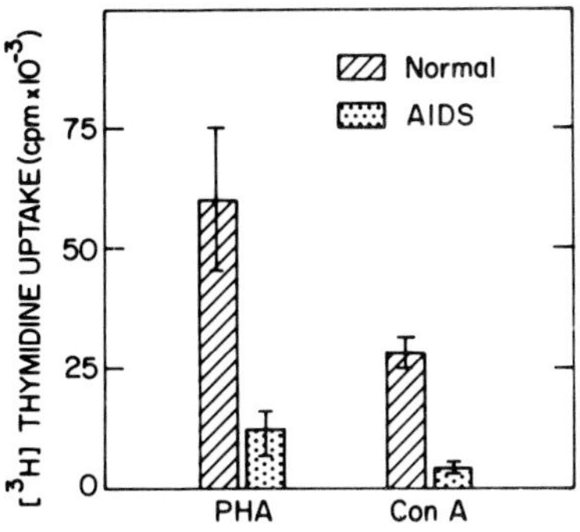
[³H] THYMIDINE UPTAKE (cpm x10⁻³)
75
50
25
0
Normal
AIDS
PHA
Con A

Fig. 9.18 Mitogenic responses to PHA and concanavalin A of lymphocytes from normal controls and patients with AIDS. (Based on data from Fletcher, M.A., *et al.*, (1987) *Diagn. Clin. Immunol.*, 5, 69–81.)

such as secretion of lymphokines or induction of effector cells. Another application of mitogenic lectins is for the preparation of chromosome maps for karyotyping, sex determination and detection of chromosomal defects, since in the stimulated cell the chromosomes are easily visualized (Fig. 4.2).

9.6.3 Bone marrow transplanation

Cell separation by soybean agglutinin (section 9.4) proved to be the key to the breakthrough which permitted, eventually, bone marrow transplants between genetically non-identical individuals. Until about 1980, bone marrow transplants presented a formidable challenge, more so, in fact, than did transplantation of organs. The difficulty lay in the nature of bone marrow, which, in addition to desired immature haematopoietic stem cells – the source of the entire blood system – also contains mature T cells. The mature cells are responsible for the lethal graft *versus* host reaction in which the transplanted bone marrow attacks the tissues of the recipient and which occurs when histoincompatible (mismatched) bone marrow is used for transplantation. In 1978 it was demonstrated in our laboratory that sequential agglutination with peanut agglutinin and soybean agglutinin of mouse bone marrow yields a fraction that is enriched in haematopoietic stem cells and is devoid of mature T cells. The stem cell enriched fraction prepared from one strain of mice was successfully implanted into lethally irradiated mice of another strain, resulting in nearly 100% survival of the treated animals. In contrast, almost all irradiated mice that were transplanted with unfractionated splenocytes died. These results suggested that lectin fractionation may also be adapted for the removal of T cells from human bone marrow. It has indeed been found that soybean agglutinin effectively removes from human marrow the majority of the cells responsible for graft *versus* host disease, the main cause of mortality in patients treated with allogeneic bone marrow. By now, bone marrow separated with soybean agglutinin has been successfully transplanted into over 100

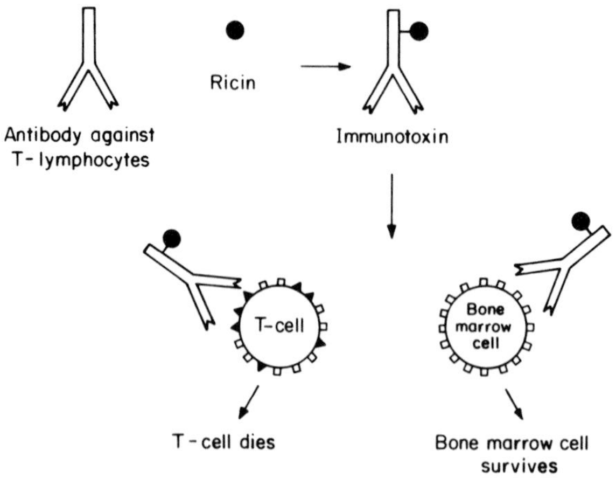
Ricin
Antibody against T-lymphocytes
Immunotoxin
T-cell
Bone marrow cell
T-cell dies
Bone marrow cell survives

Fig. 9.19 Elimination of mature T cells from bone marrow with the aid of an anti-T immunotoxin. (Modified from Blakey, D.C. and Thorpe, P.E. (1986) *BioEssays*, **4**, 292–7.)

children born with severe combined immune deficiency (known as 'bubble children' because they have to be kept in absolute isolation in plastic chambers to prevent infection). Without this treatment most of them would have died for lack of matched donors. More than 70% of these children have been cured and lead a normal life [74]. The method is now being tested in leukaemia patients, with encouraging results. It was also used in Moscow in May 1986, in the attempts to save the lives of the lethally irradiated victims of the Chernobyl accident. Both of the two surviving transplanted victims received bone marrow that had been treated with soybean agglutinin.

In another approach, T cell depletion of donor bone marrow has been achieved by treatment with an immunotoxin consisting of ricin and antibodies to T lymphocytes (Fig. 9.19). In a study of 17 patients with high risk leukaemias, who received transplants of sibling bone marrow treated with the above immunotoxin, none developed severe graft *versus* host disease [75].

9.7 LECTINS IN SPACE BIOLOGY

The mitogenic activity of lectins has provided a simple means to assess the effect of space flight on the functioning of the immune system of man. The response of lymphocytes of space crews to concanavalin A after a space flight was much lower (by up to 60%) than that of lymphocytes from blood drawn before the flight; response to the mitogen usually returned to normal within two weeks after landing [10]. The decrease in response was even greater when cells in culture, exposed to concanavalin A during the space flight, were compared with control cell cultures stimulated for the same period of time on the ground (Fig. 9.20). To establish whether this decrease is due to exposure of the cells to zero gravity or to other

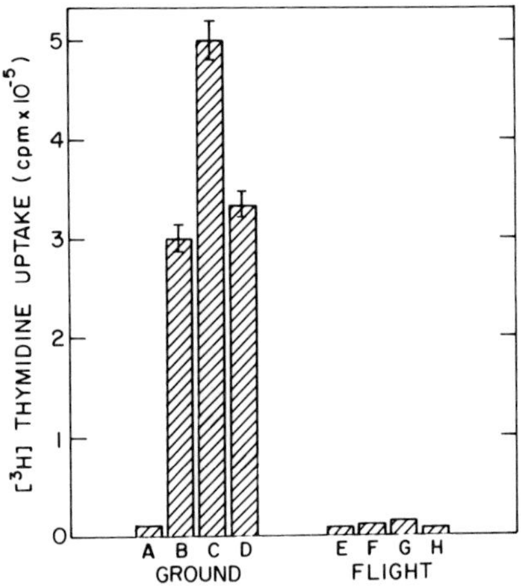
[^{3}H] THYMIDINE UPTAKE (cpm x 10^{-5})
0
1
2
3
4
5
A B C D
GROUND
E F G H
FLIGHT

Fig. 9.20 Effect of zero gravity on stimulation of lymphocytes by concanavalin A. Cultures of human lymphocytes were exposed to mitogenic concentrations of the lectin on the ground (samples B, C, D) and in space (samples F, G, H), respectively. Samples A (ground) and E (space) are unstimulated controls. (Reproduced with permission from Cogoli, A. and Tschopp A. (1985) *Immunol. Today*, **6**, 1–4.)

inflight factors, lymphocytes cultured with concanavalin A in space under conditions of zero gravity were compared with controls maintained in flight but under simulated 1 G gravity conditions, as well as with cells stimulated on the ground. In addition, blood drawn from crew members during the flight, three days after launch, was cultured with concanavalin A both under zero gravity and simulated 1 G gravity. In all cultures kept under zero gravity, practically no stimulation occurred. Furthermore, activation of the lymphocytes of the crew members was markedly depressed in the inflight samples, compared with the preflight values. These results demonstrate that lymphocytes maintained at zero gravity are not stimulated and confirm the earlier findings that the immune system of astronauts is adversely affected by space conditions.

CHAPTER 10
Lectin resistant cells

The cytotoxic properties exhibited by certain lectins make them ideal agents for selection of clones of animal cell mutants with altered surface carbohydrates. Such clones are obtained by culturing the cells on solid media in the presence of toxic concentrations of a lectin, and picking up the few colonies that survive (Fig. 10.1). The lectin resistant cells thus selected are stable, grow easily in the

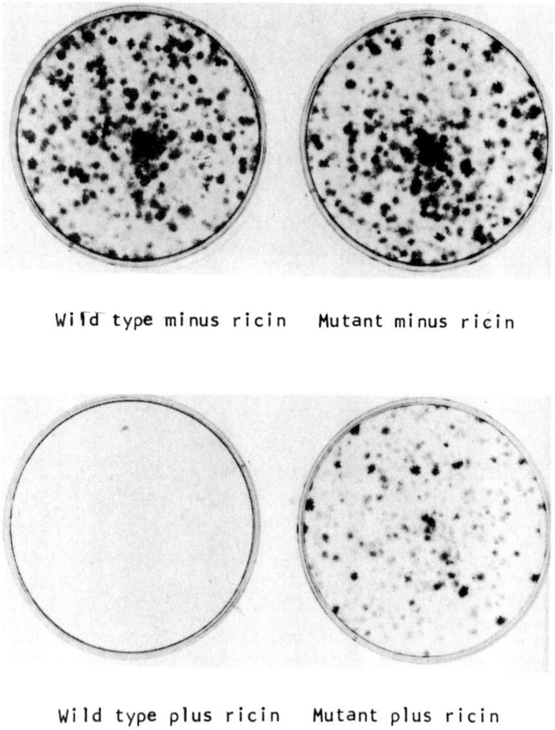
Wild type minus ricin
Mutant minus ricin
Wild type plus ricin
Mutant plus ricin

Fig. 10.1 Selection of lectin resistant mutants. (Courtesy R. Colin Hughes.)

laboratory and provide a new tool for studying the genetics, biosynthesis and functions of cell surface glycoconjugates [76, 77].

10.1 GLYCOSYLATION PATHWAYS

The lectin-resistance of most mutants is due to a decrease or complete loss of the ability to bind the lectin used for their selection. There are two general ways in which surface oligosaccharides may be structurally modified so that the cells no longer bind lectins: the sugars to which the lectins originally bound may be masked, e.g. by covalent attachment of other sugar residues, or they may be deleted. Deletion of cell surface sugars is the most common cause of resistance and results from the loss of one of the enzymes that participate in the normal pathway of protein glycosylation (Fig. 10.2). Several mutants of Chinese hamster ovary (CHO) or baby hamster kidney (BHK) cells have been selected for their resistance to wheat germ agglutinin, ricin, PHA or lentil lectin. Such cells show a concomitant increase in mannose content and, as a result, are more sensitive to concanavalin A cytotoxicity than are the wild type cells. Studies with these mutants have been of particular significance in the elucidation of certain aspects of the processing pathways operating in the biosynthesis of complex *N*-glycosidic oligosaccharide chains. Among the major findings was the demonstration that two distinct *N*-acetylglucosaminyltransferases (I and II) are involved in the attachment of *N*-acetylglucosamine residues to the $\alpha1 \rightarrow 3$ and $\alpha1 \rightarrow 6$-linked mannose residues, respectively, in the pentasaccharide core of *N*-glycosidic oligosaccharides. No less significant was the demonstration that the attachment of the first *N*-acetylglucosamine residue (to the $\alpha1 \rightarrow 3$-linked mannose) by transferase I serves as a key control point: it determines whether further processing, leading to the formation of outer branches containing *N*-acetylglucosamine, galactose (and sometimes also sialic acid) will take place or whether the carbohydrate units will contain oligomannosyl chains instead. Several of the mutants were shown to lack transferase I, which completely accounted for the complex profile of multiple lectin resistance and concanavalin A supersensitivity (Fig. 10.2).

Other ricin resistant mutants of BHK cells lack a different processing enzyme, α-mannosidase II, and accumulate hybrid glycans instead of complex type chains, also in agreement with established pathways of glycoprotein maturation (Fig. 10.2). Some lectin resistant mutants exhibit altered glycosylation patterns for reasons other than loss of glycosyltransferases or processing glycosidases. Among these is a mutant that lacks the enzyme required for the synthesis of dolichol phosphomannose (Dol-P-Man) from guanosine diphosphomannose (GDP-Man) and dolichol phosphate. Since Dol-P-Man is the donor of four out of the nine mannose residues of the lipid linked oligosaccharide donor for *N*-glycosylation (Fig. 9.12), this mutant synthesizes a truncated oligosaccharide with just five mannose residues. As a result, its glycoproteins contain large amounts of an *N*-linked oligosaccharide, $Man_5GlcNAc_2$, not normally found in animal cells.

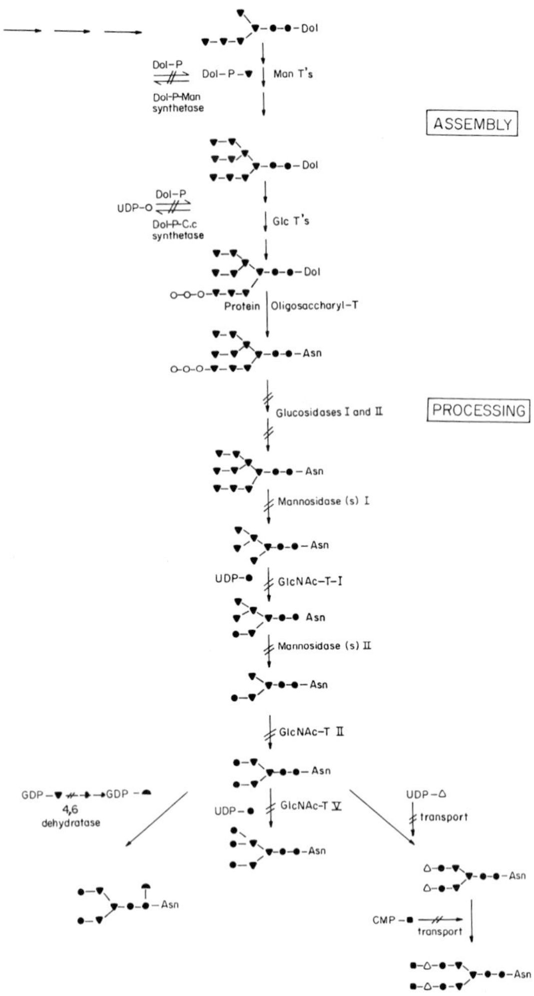
Dol
Dol–P
Dol–P–▼
Man T's
Dol-P-Man
synthetase
ASSEMBLY
Dol
Dol–P
UDP–O
Dol-P-C.c
synthetase
Glc T's
Dol
Protein
Oligosaccharyl–T
Asn
Glucosidases I and II
PROCESSING
Asn
Mannosidase (s) I
Asn
UDP–●
GlcNAc–T–I
Asn
Mannosidase (s) II
Asn
GlcNAc–T II
Asn
GDP
GDP
4,6
dehydratase
UDP–●
GlcNAc-T V
UDP–Δ
transport
Asn
Asn
Asn
CMP
transport
Asn

Fig. 10.2 Enzymatic steps involved in the assembly and processing of N-glycosidic units of glycoproteins. Dashed lines denote reactions blocked in some lectin resistant mutants. D, dolichol; T, transferase. (Modified from Stanley, P. (1987) *Trends Genet.*, 3, 77–81.)

Mutants of another class, selected for their resistance to pea lectin, are characterized by a virtually total absence of L-fucose, a constituent of both *N*- and O-linked carbohydrate units of glycoproteins. These mutants are specifically deficient in GDP-mannose-4, 6-dehydratase, an enzyme that participates in the conversion of GDP-mannose to GDP-L-fucose (Fig. 10.2). It may be recalled that the presence of L-fucose in a glycoprotein is required for the binding of pea lectin; therefore, deficiency of this sugar fully explains the resistance of the mutants to the lectin.

With the exception of the lesion just described, the mutations hitherto discussed affect only reactions involved in the synthesis of *N*-linked carbohydrates. Studies with a group of mutants selected for their resistance to wheat germ agglutinin and/or PHA, on the other hand, were of help in clarifying aspects of glycosylation reactions that also affect the structure of O-linked moieties of glycoproteins as well as the carbohydrates of glycolipids and proteoglycans. These mutants are deficient in sialic acid or in both sialic acid and galactose (Fig. 10.2). Interestingly, they possess all the components needed for sialylation and galactosylation, i.e. the nucleotide donors [cytidine monophospho-(CMP)-*N*-acetylneuraminic acid and UDP-galactose], acceptors and transferases, and the lesion responsible for the impaired incorporation of sialic acid and galactose was until recently unknown. It has now been found that these mutants are unable to translocate the respective sugar nucleotides from the cytosol, where they are synthesized, into the lumen of Golgi vesicles where the sugar is transferred from the donor to the carbohydrate chains of glycoconjugates [78]. Although translocation of nucleotides across the Golgi membrane has been demonstrated *in vitro* with purified Golgi vesicles from a variety of cells (e.g. rat liver or mouse thymocytes), its occurrence *in vivo* has not been proven. The fact that mutants in which this process is impaired synthesize altered carbohydrate structures provides convincing evidence that such translocation is physiologically important. Experiments with isolated vesicles have shown that in each of the mutants the translocation of only one nucleotide (CMP-*N*-acetylneuraminic acid or UDP-galactose) is impaired, leading to the conclusion that there are separate transport systems or channels for different nucleotide sugars. It is therefore apparent that in the mutants lacking both sialic acid and galactose, the deficiency of the former is a secondary outcome of the lack of galactosylation (which is a prerequisite for the attachment of sialic acid).

10.2 FUNCTIONS OF CELL SURFACE SUGARS

In addition to serving as useful tools for the investigation of the biosynthesis of carbohydrate units of glycoproteins, studies with lectin resistant mutants provide insight into the biological functions of cell surface sugars. The very fact that cell mutants with severely truncated *N*-oligosaccharide chains can be isolated is compelling evidence that the complex *N*-linked chains are not necessary for cell viability. On the other hand, no mutant has been found that is more than threefold as resistant to concanavalin A as the wild type cells. This may mean that alterations in cell surface sugars, which would lead to lower sensitivity to this lectin are lethal to the cells. In other words, a minimal level of surface oligosaccharides of the type to which concanavalin A binds appears to be essential for cell viability.

Lectin resistant mutants have been used to characterize certain aspects of virus production and of virus–cell interactions. For example, when enveloped viruses, such as vesicular stomatitis virus or Sindbis virus were grown in cell mutants that are unable to synthesize complex carbohydrate chains, the oligosaccharides of the virion envelope glycoproteins exhibited the same defects as the mutant cells in which they were produced. This unequivocally demonstrates that viral oligosaccharides are synthesized by host enzymes rather than by virus specified enzymes. Furthermore, since the virions of the vesicular stomatitis virus produced in these mutant cells were fully infectious, it is evident that the outer branches of the complex oligosaccharides of viral glycoproteins are not necessary for viral assembly or infectivity.

A wheat germ agglutinin resistant CHO cell line, characterized by a general lack of sialic acid, could neither bind Sendai virus nor fuse with it. Another variant of the same cells, which lacked sialic acid in *N*-glycosidic chains but carried this sugar on *O*-glycosidic ones, could be fused by the Sendai virus, but not by the Newcastle disease virus. It appears therefore that the receptor for the former virus is on *O*-linked carbohydrate units, while that for the latter virus is on *N*-glycosidic carbohydrate units.

Lectin resistant mutants are being employed in attempts to further our understanding of the relationship between cell surfaces and neoplasia. For example, melanoma cell mutants resistant to wheat germ agglutinin showed a dramatic decrease in metastasizing capacity through both lymphatic and vascular channels. The tumourigenicity of the mutants was also decreased in comparison with that of the parental melanoma cells. A ricin resistant mutant selected from the same parental cells as the wheat germ agglutinin resistant one displayed a decrease in the spread of metastases through the blood stream, but no change in its capacity to metastasize *via* the lymphatic route. Another study employed a wheat germ agglutinin resistant mutant selected from a highly metastatic murine tumour cell line; this mutant was non-metastatic when injected into mice. The biochemical basis of the mutation was found to be impaired translocation of UDP-galactose into the Golgi. As a consequence, the *N*-linked complex oligosaccharides produced by the mutant cells lacked both galactose and *N*-acetylneuraminic acid. By taking advantage of the hypersensitivity of this mutant to *Griffonia simplicifolia* lectin II (specific for *N*-acetylglucosamine), a single step revertant was selected; this revertant simultaneously regained the sialylated *N*-acetyllactosamine branches of the *N*-linked oligosaccharides and the highly metastatic phenotype [79]. A series of mutants of the same murine tumour cell line with dramatically decreased metastatic potential was selected on the basis of their resistance to L-PHA. They lacked the enzyme *N*-acetylglucosaminetransferase V which attaches a $\beta 1 \rightarrow 6$ *N*-acetylglucosamine to the $\alpha 1 \rightarrow 6$-linked mannose in the pentasaccharide core [80]. As a result, the mutants exhibited a subtle glycosylation defect in that the outer $\beta 1 \rightarrow 6$-linked branch was missing. Thus, these studies with lectin resistant mutants have provided the first clear cut evidence for an association between the expression of specific carbohydrate structures and metastasis.

CHAPTER 11
Functions in nature

The ubiquitous occurrence of lectins in nature and their ability to discriminate between closely related saccharides in solution and on cell surfaces provided a major stimulus for the continuing search for their physiological function(s). A strong argument that lectins indeed have such functions is the fact that they have been conserved throughout evolution as homologous families of proteins. Another argument is that many of them are developmentally regulated and that their appearance often coincides with a distinct physiological change in the life of an organism. Notably, the putative receptors for the lectins, i.e. complementary carbohydrate structures, are frequently also under strict developmental control.

Speculations about possible functions were originally confined to lectins from plants, until recently the only kingdom in which these proteins were known to be common constituents. The early ideas were summarized by Boyd in 1963 [81]. Perhaps the most naive of these was that because lectins behave as antibodies, they are antibodies, notwithstanding the fact that plants do not have an immune system. Another point of view assumed that the carbohydrate binding properties of lectins are merely an accidental feature of their structure and that these proteins are just storage materials. It is a telling reflection on our continuing lack of understanding of the roles of plant lectins that this idea is still with us. Another old speculation still alive today is that lectins might function as 'carbohydrate catchers' and thereby aid in the transport of carbohydrates and their immobilization in the seeds. No evidence to support or refute this idea is available.

At present, the most popular belief is that lectins, whether free or membrane bound, function primarily as recognition molecules and that they act by combining with complementary carbohydrates in solution or on cells. This recognition function may be expressed differently in different organisms and also in separate organs or tissues of the same organism, and the particular purpose of the lectin mediated recognition may not necessarily be the same in different systems. For example, the lectin and the complementary carbohydrate may be on cells of the same type (homotypic) or of different types (heterotypic) (Fig. 11.1). Membrane bound lectins may interact with carbohydrates, either on soluble glycoproteins that act as bridges between the cells, or on insoluble components of the extracellular matrix, thus promoting cell–substrate adhesion.

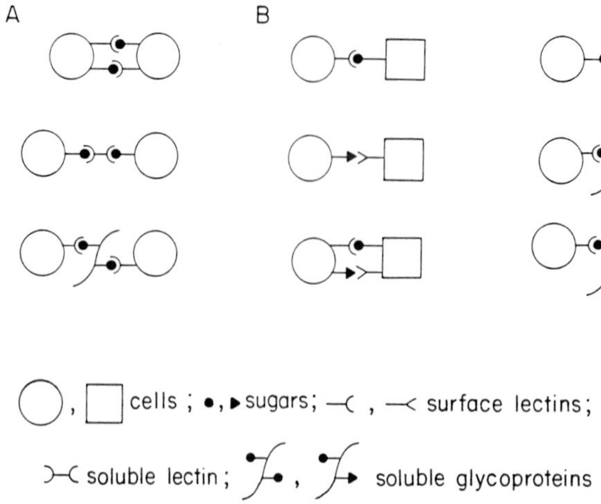
A
B
cells ; sugars; surface lectins;
soluble lectin ; soluble glycoproteins

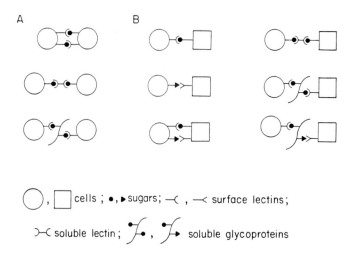

Fig. 11.1 Different modes of cell–molecule and cell–cell interactions mediated by lectins: A. between cells of the same kind (homotypic); B. between cells of different kinds (heterotypic).

11.1 IN PLANTS

In plants, two proposed functions of lectins are currently attracting most attention [82]: (a) as mediators of symbiosis between nitrogen fixing microorganisms, primarily rhizobia, and plants; and (b) in protection of plants against phytopathogens.

11.1.1 Symbiosis

The association between legumes and nitrogen fixing bacteria, such as rhizobia (Fig. 11.2), is highly specific: legume species of cultivars which are nodulated by some *Rhizobium* isolates are not nodulated by others. For example, rhizobia that infect and nodulate soybeans cannot nodulate garden peas or white clover, and *vice versa*. The successful infection of legumes by their bacterial symbionts is of immense importance both in the nitrogen cycle of terrestial life and from the economic point of view.

The assumption that lectins are responsible for legume–rhizobia association was originally based on the finding that a lectin from a particular legume, for example soybean agglutinin, binds in a sugar specific manner to the corresponding rhizobial species and not to bacteria that infect other legumes. Additional experiments with lectins from the seeds of four legumes (soybean, pea, red kidney bean and jack bean) and lipopolysaccharides from the respective symbionts, have shown that the bacterial lipopolysaccharide bound only to the lectin from the legume with which the bacterium forms a symbiotic relationship. It was therefore assumed that

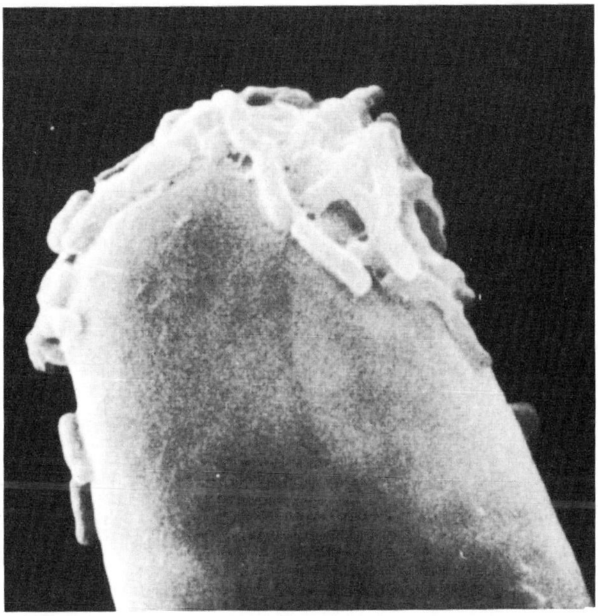

Fig. 11.2 Scanning electron micrograph of phase I attachment of *Rhizobium trifolii* 0403 to the tip of a clover root hair after 15 min incubation. (Reproduced with permission from Dazzo, F.B. and Brill, W.J. (1979) *J. Bacteriol.*, **137**, 1362–73.)

attachment of the rhizobia to the plant roots occurs by the direct interaction between bacterial surface carbohydrates and lectins present in the plant roots. This is supported by the recent demonstration that a cultured cell line, derived from soybean roots, bound *Rhizobium japonicum* and that the binding was specifically inhibited by galactose [83]. These cells produced an endogenous galactose specific lectin (probably identical with the soybean seed lectin) which was localized on the cell wall and therefore accessible to the external environment.

A different mode of action of lectins in plant–symbiont attachment has been proposed on the basis of studies of the interaction between *Rhizobium trifolii* and white clover [84]. According to this proposal, the lectin serves as a bridge between common or similar carbohydrate structures present on the surfaces of both the root tips and the bacteria. Such a receptor was shown to be present on the cell surfaces of infective strains of *Rhizobium trifolii* but absent (or inaccessible) in non-infective strains. It has also been found that extracts of clover seeds and seedling roots contain a lectin called trifoliin, capable of binding to infective, but not to uninfective, strains of rhizobia. Anti-lectin antibodies bound mostly to the root hair region of clover roots but did not bind to roots of other legumes, such as alfalfa and vetch.

Other findings, however, cast serious doubts on the validity of the notion that lectins serve as recognition molecules in host–symbiont interactions in leguminous plants. For instance, no evidence was found for the preferential binding of concanavalin A to rhizobia strains capable of nodulating jack bean. Also, not all soybean nodulating strains of *Rhizobium japonicum* bind soybean agglutinin, whereas several non-nodulating strains have been found to bind the lectin. More importantly, soybean lines that lack the lectin still possess the ability to be nodulated by symbiotic *Rhizobium japonicum* strains. There are additional examples of inconsistencies between various studies that purport either to support or to refute the lectin recognition hypothesis, which continues therefore to be the subject of considerable debate.

11.1.2 Protection

The proposal that lectins may be involved in the protection of plants against pathogenic microorganisms was originally based on the observation that wheat germ agglutinin binds to *N*-acetylglucosamine residues on hyphal tips and hyphal septa of *Trichoderma viride* and inhibits fungal growth. It was subsequently found that potato lectin acts in a similar manner on *Botrytis cinerea*, and that wheat germ, peanut and soybean agglutinins inhibit incorporation of acetate, *N*-acetylglucosamine and galactose into young hyphae of *Aspergillus ochraceus*. In a more extensive study [85], eleven purified lectins representing all the major groups of lectin specificity, caused growth disruption during germination of spores of *Neurospora crassa, Aspergillus amstelodami* and *Botryodiplodia theobromae*. According to a recent report, however, the inhibitory activity of wheat germ agglutinin and potato lectin, as well as of other lectins specific for chitin oligosaccharides, is most likely due to contamination with the enzyme chitinase which is a potent inhibitor of fungal growth [86]. Such contamination is apt to occur since the lectins and enzyme have similar specificities and will therefore behave similarly on the affinity chromatography columns used for the purification of the lectins. This criticism still does not invalidate the results obtained with lectins such as peanut and soybean agglutinins which are specific for sugars other than oligomers of *N*-acetylglucosamine.

11.2 IN VERTEBRATE ANIMALS

A variety of roles have been ascribed to animal lectins. Some of these, such as the control of glycoprotein traffic in the body are well documented, while others, e.g. the regulation of organ formation or involvement in metastasis, require more solid evidence.

11.2.1 Glycoprotein traffic

Membrane bound lectins, several of which have been well characterized, mediate the binding of soluble extracellular and intracellular glycoproteins to membranes, and in this way control glycoprotein traffic, both within the cells and between different organs in the body. The classical examples are the binding of asialoglycoproteins by a galactose specific mammalian lectin on rabbit liver cells, and of asialo-agalactoglycoproteins by mannose/*N*-acetylglucosamine specific lectins on avian hepatocytes; both interactions are probably key steps in the removal of such glycoproteins from the circulatory system of the respective animals. Another example is the pinocytosis of glycoproteins with terminal non-reducing mannose and/or *N*-acetylglucosamine residues by macrophages. This uptake is mediated by a macrophage surface lectin specific for mannose and *N*-acetylglucosamine. The same lectin is probably also responsible for the binding of yeasts to phagocytes and their killing by these cells.

The mannose-6-phosphate specific lectins mediate the transport of phosphorylated hydrolases to lysosomes [87]. Like all other glycoproteins, these enzymes, too, mature in the Golgi apparatus. In the course of maturation, they acquire a unique marker, the mannose-6-phosphate recognition signal, which is attached to their *N*-linked oligomannose units. Through this marker they bind to the mannose-6-phosphate specific lectins and are targeted to their subcellular destination, the lysosomes. The lectins are also present on cell surfaces, where they function in the uptake of lysosomal enzymes that, for one reason or another, have been secreted from the cells. Proof for the biological significance of this pathway emerged from studies of the rare hereditary disease known as I cell disease. Although patients with this disease produce normal levels of the hydrolases, they cannot attach the mannose-6-phosphate marker to the enzymes that are therefore not recognized by the mannose-6-phosphate specific lectins. As a result the enzymes, instead of being targeted to the lysosymes, are secreted from the cells and cannot be taken up again. The lack of lysosomal enzymes inside the cell leads to accumulation of abnormal metabolites, with overall results ranging from mild retardation to death. The I cell disease thus provides what is probably the best evidence for the participation of a lectin in a physiological process.

11.2.2 Migration of lymphocytes

Animal cell surface lectins apparently have other functions as well. One of these is the control of cell migration in the body. A case in point is the lymphocytes. During their normal lifespan, these cells migrate from the bloodstream into the lymphoid organs, such as lymph nodes and Peyers patches. An adhesive interaction between lymphocytes and the endothelium of postcapillary venules is the first step in this migratory or 'homing' process. Insight into the molecular basis of the adhesive interaction was obtained by experiments *in vitro*, which demonstrated that binding of rat lymphocytes to frozen sections of syngeneic lymph nodes was inhibited by L-fucose and mannose-6-phosphate, as well as by fucoidin, a polymer of L-fucose, and a phosphomannosyl-rich polysaccharide from yeasts [88]. Fucoidin also blocked the migration of lymphocytes into lymph nodes *in vivo*. Thus, the recognition between lymphocytes and the cells of the lymphoid organs is based on sugar–lectin interactions.

Another case of carbohydrate specific 'homing' appears to be the migration of haematopoietic progenitor (stem) cells to stromal cells of spleen and marrow. The specific binding of the progenitor cells to the haematopoietic stroma is a prerequisite for their proliferation and differentiation. Synthetically prepared glycoproteins (neoglycoproteins) containing galactose or mannose residues inhibited the binding of granulocyte-macrophage progenitor cells to marrow stroma in long term bone marrow culture and their subsequent proliferation and differentiation [89].

A β-galactose specific lectin present in the epithelium of the thymus has been postulated to be responsible for holding immature (PNA^+, section 9.4) thymocytes in the cortex of this organ by binding to galactose residues on the surface of these cells. Upon maturation of the thymocytes, the galactose residues become masked by attachment of sialic acid, the cells lose their ability to bind the lectin and thus are free to migrate to the thymic medulla, where the mature (PNA^-) thymocytes reside, or directly to the periphery.

11.2.3 Metastasis

Lectins present on various human and murine metastatic tumour cells are thought to influence the pathogenesis of cancer metastasis [90–92]. These lectins may promote the formation of tumour cell aggregates (or emboli) in the circulation by combining with carbohydrate residues on apposing cells. In addition, they may facilitate the adhesion of the aggregates to the endothelial layer of the capillaries. For instance, a good correlation was found between the amount of the galactose specific lectin expressed on melanoma cells (as measured by their ability to undergo aggregation in the presence of asialofetuin and by the extent of binding of monoclonal anti-lectin antibody) and the formation of pulmonary metastases after intravenous injection of the cells into syngeneic mice. Quite significantly, cells which have been pretreated with the anti-lectin antibody showed a decreased metastatic potential [90].

11.2.4 Differentiation and organ formation

A common function proposed for the soluble vertebrate lectins is to bind to the complementary glycoconjugates on and around the cells that release them and thus control the organization of the extracellular matrix and perhaps also organ formation. These lectins are initially concentrated inside cells, but are ultimately found extracellularly. For example, chicken lactose lectin I, which is concentrated intracellularly in developing muscle, becomes extracellular with maturation. Likewise, a rat β-galactoside binding lectin in lung is concentrated in elastic fibres, a specialized form of extracellular matrix.

As mentioned before, a strong argument for a physiological function of lectins in animals is the pronounced parallel in the appearance and cellular distribution of lectins and complementary carbohydrate structures in many developing organs and tissues. A striking illustration is the appearance of two lectins in neurons of the dorsal root ganglion soon after formation of the ganglia, both of which are restricted to a distinct functional subset of the neurons. The same cells also express a series of developmentally regulated carbohydrate structures, for which the lectins are specific, that differ from those found in other subsets of dorsal root ganglion neurons [93].

Another system in which a lectin plays an important role is erythroid development. A β-galactose specific lectin present on the surface of erythroblasts allows them to cluster into 'erythroblastic islands' in the vicinity of a macrophage 'nurse' cell. This aggregation is a necessary step in the maturation of the erythroblasts into reticulocytes, the direct precursors of erythrocytes, which are released from the aggregates and enter the blood stream. The concentration of the lectin at the cell surface decreases with maturation of the erythroblasts and the release of the reticulocytes. In this system, too, there are extensive changes in galactose containing carbohydrate sequences during the differentiation process.

11.2.5 Fertilization

The attachment of a sperm to an egg, the first step in fertilization, is another example of a fundamental process in which lectins have been implicated [94]. The strict species specificity of the sperm–egg interaction prompted the speculation that the initial step requires recognition between carbohydrates on the surface of the egg and lectins in the sperm plasma membrane. Some evidence to support this assumption has recently been obtained. In the mouse, the carbohydrate determinant is in the form of O-linked oligosaccharide chains of a glycoprotein found in the zona pellucida (the thick extracellular coat) of the egg; the sperm lectin has not yet been identified.

11.3 IN INVERTEBRATES

As mentioned, humoral lectins are ubiquitous within invertebrates (section 3.1.3). Since invertebrates lack immunoglobulins, it has been suggested that the humoral lectins might be their functional analogues [95, 96]. Recent studies with insect lectins have indeed demonstrated that they may participate in the elimination of foreign bodies from larvae and pupae. The lectin isolated from the haemolymph of the flesh fly larvae was induced under two different physiological conditions, on injury of the body wall of the larvae and on pupation [97]. A relatively high level of lectin was maintained during the entire pupal stage but decreased rapidly before emergence and no lectin was found in the mature fly. The lectin participated in the removal of sheep red blood cells introduced into the abdominal cavity of the larvae. It also activated mouse marrow cells to kill *Candida parapsilosis* cells as well as macrophages to kill tumour cells (section 4.3). In the haemolymph of pupae of the Chinese oak silk moth *Antheraea pernyi* a lectin is present [98], the concentration of which increased markedly with time after injection of a suspension of *Escherichia coli* into the pupae, indicating that it could be involved in the defence mechanisms of the pupae.

11.4 IN SLIME MOLDS

Aggregation of slime molds, a key event in the differentiation of these organisms from their single cell, vegetative form to an aggregated form, was for over a decade considered as perhaps the most convincing evidence for the involvement of lectins in cell–cell recognition. This notion was based primarily on studies with *Dictyostelium discoideum* (Fig. 11.3), and its developmentally regulated galactose specific lectin, discoidin I [99]. Neither the lectin, nor the mRNA that directs its synthesis, appear to be present at significant levels during vegetative growth; both become prominent as the mold passes from the vegetative to the aggregating stage, whereupon the cells adhere to each other. It was shown that the lectin is present on the surface of aggregating cells and, moreover, that in its isolated form it agglutinates aggregating slime mold cells but not the vegetative cells. Recent evidence, however, indicates that discoidin I, although intimately involved in slime mold aggregation, does not participate in this process on the basis of its ability to bind carbohydrates. Discoidin I apparently acts by a sugar independent mechanism in which it binds to the cells through a short segment of the molecule, the

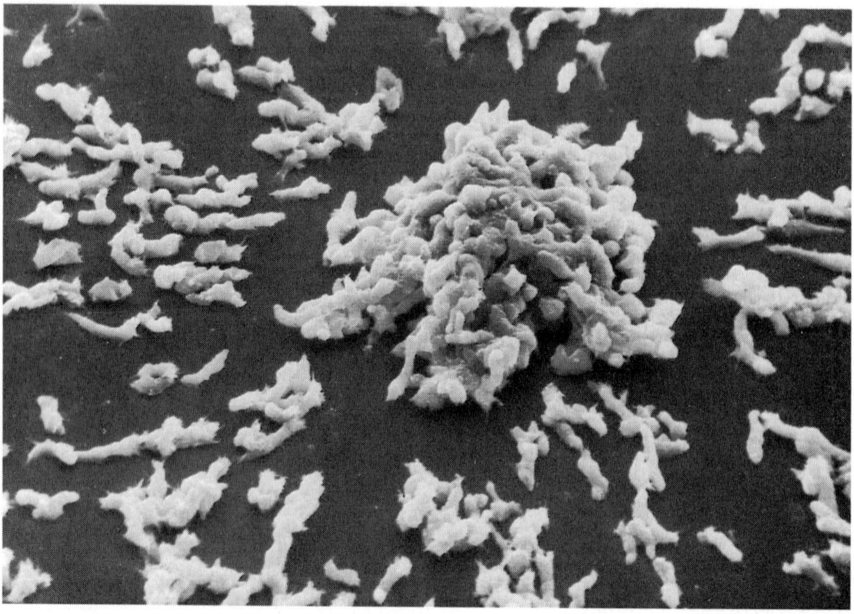

Fig. 11.3 Scanning electron micrograph of the ordered migration of *Dictyostelium discoideum* cells into an aggregate. (Courtesy of Samuel H. Barondes.)

tripeptide Arg-Gly-Asp. The same tripeptide is present in many other adhesion molecules, such as fibronectin for example, where it also constitutes the recognition site of the cell binding domain.

It is now believed that the carbohydrate binding site of discoidin I is required for packaging of the lectin into subcellular particles for eventual secretion from the cell, thus making it available to play its part in cell–cell aggregation by the mechanism described above [100].

11.5 IN PARASITES

The lectins of *Entamoeba histolytica*, the causative agent of amoebic dysentery, may be involved in the pathogenesis of the disease in several ways. They mediate the adherence of the amoebae to intestinal epithelial cells of the host, thus facilitating invasion. Once invasion has taken place and the amoebae have spread through the host, the lectins mediate the binding of the parasite to host tissues, in particular hepatocytes, initiating the killing of these cells. In addition, the lectins permit the amoebae to bind bacteria which carry the appropriate sugars; the bound bacteria serve as a source of nutrition for the parasite and increase its virulence.

11.6 IN BACTERIA

Bacterial surface lectins play a key role in the initiation of infection by mediating bacterial adherence to epithelial cells of the host, for example in the urinary (Fig. 11.4) and gastrointestinal tracts [4, 101]. This has been best documented for *Escherichia coli* carrying type 1 (mannose specific) or type P (Galα4Gal specific) fimbrial lectins, and for type 1 fimbriated *Klebsiella pneumoniae*. The fimbriated strains of these organisms are more infective than their isogenic non-fimbriated counterparts. Furthermore, sugars that inhibit binding of the bacteria to epithelial cells *in vitro*, as well as antibodies to the lectins or to the lectin receptors, decreased significantly the rate of urinary tract infection in experimental animals.

The galactose specific lectins expressed by oral Actinomyces such as *Actinomyces naeslundii* and *Actinomyces viscosus*, facilitate the initial colonization of the epithelial surfaces of the mouth and of the teeth by these organisms. Such colonization is the result of attachment of the bacteria *via* their surface lectins to galactose residues either on the surface of the epithelial cells, or on the surface of *Streptococcus sanguis* which are adsorbed to the enamel of the teeth.

Lectin carrying bacteria may also bind to sugars on phagocytic cells, such as human polymorphonuclear leukocytes or mouse peritoneal macrophages. As demonstrated extensively with type 1 fimbriated *Escherichia coli*, and more recently also with oral Actinomyces [102], binding frequently results in metabolic activation of the phagocytes, engulfment of the bacteria and eventual bacterial death. This sequence of events is characteristic for the well studied phagocytosis

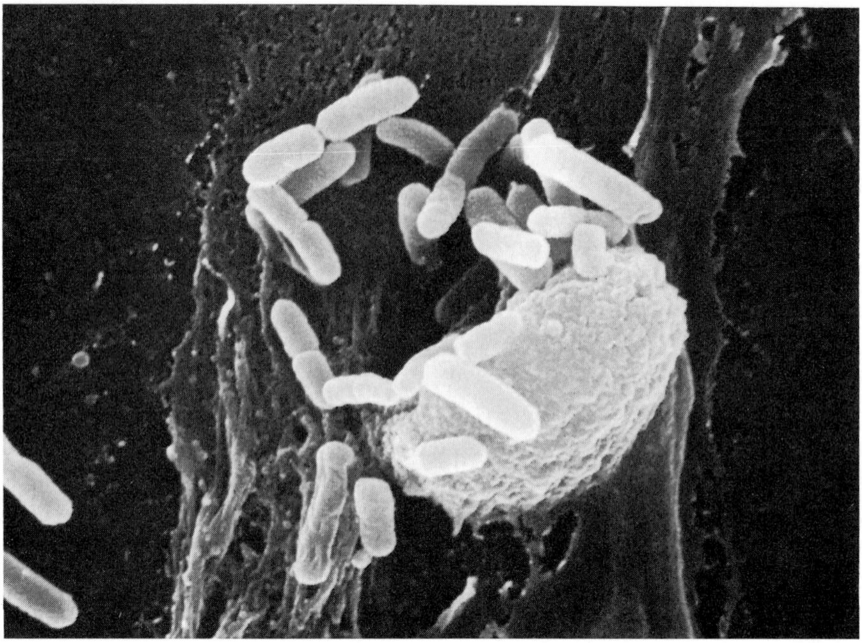

Fig. 11.4 Adhesion of *Escherichia coli* to kidney epithelial cells. (Reproduced with permission from Iwahi, T., Abe, Y. and Tsuchiya, K. (1982) *J. Med. Microbiol.*, **15**, 303–16.)

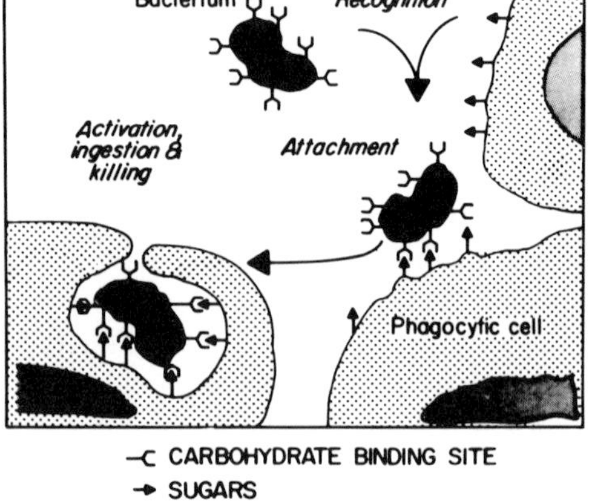
Bacterium
Recognition
Activation, ingestion & killing
Attachment
Phagocytic cell
CARBOHYDRATE BINDING SITE
SUGARS

Fig. 11.5 Phagocytosis of bacteria mediated by bacterial lectins (lectinophagocytosis). (Courtesy of Itzhak Ofek.)

mediated by opsonins, i.e. antibody and complement. The lectin mediated, non-opsonic phagocytosis, which has been designated as lectinophagocytosis, may be of clinical relevance in non-immune hosts and in tissues, such as the renal medulla, where opsonic activity is poor (Fig. 11.5) [103].

11.7 IN VIRUSES

Influenza virus haemagglutinin is another of the very few lectins for which a biological role has been unequivocally demonstrated. The lectin binds to sialic acid containing receptors on the surface of the target cells to initiate the infectious cycle [51]. Removal of sialic acid from the cells by sialidase abolishes binding and prevents infection. Furthermore, enzymatic reattachment of sialic acid or insertion of sialic acid containing oligosaccharides to the sialidase treated cells restores binding of the virus and susceptibility of the cells to infection.

CHAPTER 12
Epilogue

One hundred years have passed since the first lectin was described in castor seeds. Research on lectins has, in particular during the last decade or two, greatly enriched our knowledge in different areas of biochemistry, plant physiology, microbiology and immunology. It has also provided us with powerful tools for biological and medical investigations in such diverse areas as the structural characterization of glycoconjugates, the tracing of neuroanatomical pathways and bone marrow transplantation. There is little doubt that as we learn more about lectins, and discover new ones, novel and unexpected applications can be anticipated. We may also look forward to a time when lectins with desired specificities will be designed and produced by recombinant DNA techniques.

Despite the enormous progress made during the first century of lectin research, many questions remain to be answered. For example, what are the structures of the combining sites of lectins? Are these sites the same in different lectins with the same specificity? What are the contributions of the different forces (hydrophobic, Van der Waals, etc.) to the interactions of lectins with carbohydrates and with cells? Will lectins prove to be useful in targeting drugs to cells? Last, but not least, is the tantalizing question of the biological roles of lectins. Although we have some indication as to their role in bacteria and vertebrates, little is known with certainty about the role of lectins in plants or in invertebrates, where they are so widely distributed. The continued intense activity in the field of lectin research gives grounds for hopes that at least some of these riddles will be solved in the not too distant future.

References

1. *The Lectins: Properties, Functions and Applications in Biology and Medicine*, Liener, I.E., Sharon, N. and Goldstein, I.J., eds (1986) Academic Press, Orlando, 600pp.
2. Lectins as molecules and as tools. Lis, H. and Sharon, N. (1986) *Ann. Rev. Biochem.*, 55, 35–67.
3. Plant lectins: molecular and biological aspects. Etzler, M.E. (1985) *Ann. Rev. Plant Physiol.*, **36**, 209–34.
4. *Microbial Lectins and Agglutinins: Properties and Biological Activity*, Mirelman, D., ed. (1986) J. Wiley and Sons, New York, 443pp.
5. *Vertebrate Lectins*, Olden, K. and Parent, J.B., eds (1987) Van Nostrand Reinhold, New York, 255pp.

5a. *Advances in Lectin Research*. Vol. 1, Franz, H., ed. (1988), Springer-Verlag, Berlin, 187pp.

6. *Glycoproteins*, Hughes, R.C. (1983) (Outline Studies in Biology), Chapman and Hall, London and New York, 95pp.
7. Historical background. Kocourek, J. (1986) In reference 1, pp. 1–32.
8. A century of lectin research (1888–1988). Sharon, N. and Lis, H. (1987), *Trends Biochem. Sci.*, **12**, 488–91.

8a. The ricin story, H. Franz in reference 5a, pp. 10–25.

9. *Human and Mammalian Cytogenetics: an Historical Perspective*, Hus, T.C. (1979) Springer-Verlag, New York, 186pp.
10. Lymphocyte reactivity during spaceflight. Cogoli, A. and Tschopp A. (1985) *Immunol. Today*, **6**, 1–4.

10a. Two distinct classes of carbohydrate-recognition domains in animal lectins. Drickamer, K. (1988) *J. Biol. Chem.*, **263**, 997–60.

11. Isolation of the galactose binding lectin that mediates the *in vitro* adherence of *Entamoeba histolytica*. Petri, W.A., Jr., Smith, R.D., Schlesinger, P.H., *et al* (1987) *J. Clin. Invest.*, **80**, 1238–44.
12. Isolation of a 220-kilodalton protein with lectin properties from a virulent strain of *Entamoeba histolytica*. Rosales-Encina, J.L., Meza, I., López-De-Léon, A., *et al* (1987) *J. Infect. Dis.*, **156**, 790–7.
13. Identification and characterization of taglin, a mannose-6-phosphate binding, trypsin-activated lectin from *Giardia lambia*. Ward, H.D., Lev, B.I., Kane, A.V., *et al* (1987) *Biochemistry*, **26**, 8669–75.
14. Interaction of animal viruses with cell surface receptors. Paulson, J.C. (1985) in: *The Receptors* (Vol. 2) (ed. P.M. Conn), Academic Press, New York, pp. 131–219.
15. Complex Carbohydrates, Ginsburg, V., ed. (1987) *Methods in Enzymology*, **138**, and earlier volumes in the series (**28**, 1973; **50**, 1978; **83**, 1982), Academic Press.

16. The role of the T3/antigen receptor complex in T-cell activation. Weiss, A., Imboden, J., Hardy, K., *et al* (1986) *Ann. Rev. Immunol.*, **4**, 593–619.
17. T-cell activation. MacDonald, H.R. and Nabholz, M. (1986) *Ann. Rev. Cell Biol.*, **2**, 231–53.
18. Signal transduction and intracellular events in T-lymphocyte activation. Isakov, N., Scholz, W. and Altman, A. (1986) *Immunology Today*, 7, 271–7.
19. The regulation of intracellular signals during lymphocyte activation. Imboden, J.B. (1988) *Immunology Today*, **9**, 17–18.
20. RNA N-glycosidase activity of ricin A-chain: mechanism of action of the toxic lectin ricin on eukaryotic ribosomes. Endo, Y. and Tsurugi, K. (1987) *J. Biol. Chem.*, **262**, 8128–30.
21. The mechanism of action of ricin and related toxic lectins on eukaryotic ribosomes: the site and the characteristics of the modification in 28 S ribosomal RNA caused by the toxins. Endo, Y., Mitsui, K., Motizuki, M. and Tsurugi, K. (1987) *J. Biol. Chem.*, **262**, 5908–12.
22. Closing in on ricin action. Olsnes, S. (1987) *Nature*, **328**, 474–5.
23. Immunotoxins. Pastan, I., Willingham, M.C. and FitzGerald, D.J.P. (1986) *Cell*, **47**, 641–8.
24. Redesigning Nature's poisons to create anti-tumor reagents. Vitetta, E.S., Fulton, R.J., May *et al* (1987) *Science*, **238**, 1098–1104.
25. Nutritional significance of lectins in the diet. Liener, I.E. (1986) in reference 1, pp. 527–52.
26. The role in food poisoning of toxins and allergens from higher plants. Pusztai, A. (1986) in: *Developments in Food Microbiology* – 2 (ed. R.K. Robinson), Elsevier, London and New York, pp. 179–94.
27. Binding of Navy bean (*Phaseolus vulgaris*) lectin to the intestinal cells of the rat and its effect on the absorption of glucose. Donatucci, D.A., Liener, I.E. and Gross, C.J. (1987) *J. Nutr.*, **117**, 2154–60.
27a. Effects of dietary soyabean (*Glycine max*) lectin and trypsin inhibitors upon the pancreas of rats. Grant, G., Watt, W.B., Stewart, J.C. and Pusztai, A. (1987) *Med. Sci. Res.*, **15**, 1197–8.
28. The elderberry (*Sambucus nigra* L.) bark lectin recognizes the Neu5Ac(α2-6) Gal/GalNAc sequence. Shibuya, N., Goldstein, I.J., Broekaert, *et al* (1987) *J. Biol. Chem.*, **262**, 1596–1601.
29. Lectin affinity high-performance liquid chromatography. Interactions of N-glycanase-released oligosaccharides with *Ricinus communis* agglutinin I and *Ricinus communis* agglutinin II. Green, E.D., Brodbeck, R.M. and Baenziger, J.U. (1987) *J. Biol. Chem.*, **262**, 12030–9.
30. Purification and characterization of a human lectin specific for penultimate galactose residues. Hamazaki, H. (1986) *J. Biol. Chem.*, **261**, 5455–9.
31. Isolation and characterization of a lectin with exclusive specificity towards mannose from snowdrop (*Galanthus nivalis*) bulbs. Van Damme, E.J.M., Allen, A.K. and Peumans, W.J. (1987) *FEBS Lett.*, **215**, 140–44.
32. Specificity of binding of three soluble rat lung lectins to substituted and unsubstituted mammalian β-galactosides. Leffler, H. and Barondes, S.H. (1986) *J. Biol. Chem.*, **261**, 10119–26.
33. Solution conformation of N-linked oligosaccharides. Homans, S.W., Dwek, R.A. and Rademacher, T.W. (1987) *Biochemistry*, **26**, 6571–8.
34. Site directed processing of N-linked oligosaccharides: the role of a three-dimensional structure. Carver, J.P. and Cumming, D.A. (1987) *Pure Appl. Chem.*, **59**, 1465–76.
35. Molecular recognition. II. The binding of the Lewis b and Y human blood group determinants to the lectin IV of *Griffonia simplicifolia*. Spohr, U., Hindsgaul, O. and Lemieux, R.U. (1985) *Can. J. Chem.*, **63**, 2644–52.

36. Separation and partial characterization of isolectins from *Datura strammonium* with different subunit composition. Broekaert, W.F., Allen, A.K. and Peumans, W.J. (1987) *FEBS Lett.*, **220**, 116–20.
37. Synthesis of mitogenic phytohaemagglutinin-L in *Escherichia coli.* Hoffman, L.M. and Donaldson, D.D. (1987) *Bio/Technology*, **5**, 157–60.
38. The $\beta 1 \rightarrow 2$-D-xylose and $\alpha 1 \rightarrow 3$-L-fucose substituted *N*-linked oligosaccharides from *Erythrina cristagalli* lectin: isolation, characterization and comparison with other legume lectins. Ashford, D., Dwek, R.A., Welply, J.K., *et al* (1987) *Eur. J. Biochem.*, **166**, 311–20.
39. Primary structure of wheat germ agglutinin isolectin 2. Peptide order deducted from X-ray structure. Wright, C.S., Gavilanes, F. and Peterson, D.L. (1984) *Biochemistry*, **23**, 280–7.
40. Structural differences in the two major wheat germ agglutinin isolectins. Wright, C.S. and Olafsdottir, S. (1986) *J. Biol. Chem.*, **261**, 7191–5.
41. Isolation and characterization of a cDNA clone encoding wheat germ agglutinin Raikhel, N.V. and Wilkins, T.A. (1987) *Proc. Natl Acad. Sci. USA*, **84**, 6745–9.
42. Membrane receptors that mediate glycoprotein endocytosis. Structure and biosynthesis. Drickamer, K. (1987) *Kidney Intern*, **32**, S167–S180.
43. Trafficking of lysosomal enzymes. Kornfeld, S. (1987) *FASEB J.*, **1**, 462–8.
44. The complete amino acid sequence of echinoidin, a lectin from the coelomic fluid of the sea urchin *Anthocidaris crassispina*: homologies with mammalian and insect lectins. Giga, Y., Ikai, A. and Takahashi, K. (1987) *J. Biol. Chem.*, **262**, 6197–203.
45. Three *fim* genes required for the regulation of length and mediation of adhesion of *Escherichia coli* type 1 fimbriae. Klemm, P. and Christiansen, G. (1987) *Mol. Gen. Genet.*, **208**, 439–45.
46. The PapG protein is the α-D-galactopyranosyl-$(1 \rightarrow 4)$-β-D-galactopyranose-binding adhesin of uropathogenic *Escherichia coli.* Lund, B., Lindberg, F., Marklund, B.-I. and Normark, S. (1987) *Proc. Natl Acad. Sci. USA*, **84**, 5898–902.
47. Nuclear magnetic resonance investigation of cadmium 113 substituted pea and lentil lectins. Bhattacharyya, L., Marchetti, P.S., Ellis, P.D. and Brewer, C.F. (1987) *J. Biol. Chem.*, **262**, 5616–21.
48. Three-dimensional structure of favin: saccharide binding-cyclic permutation in leguminous lectins. Reeke, G.N., Jr. and Becker, J.W. (1986) *Science*, **234**, 1108–11.
49. Refinement of the crystal structure of wheat germ agglutinin isolectin 2 at 1.8 Å resolution. Wright, C.S. (1987) *J. Mol. Biol.*, **194**, 501–29.
50. The three-dimensional structure of ricin at 2.8 Å. Montfort, W., Villafranca, J.E., Monzingo, A.F., *et al* (1987) *J. Biol. Chem.*, **262**, 5398–403.
51. The structure and function of the haemagglutinin membrane glycoprotein of influenza virus. Wiley, D.C. and Skehel, J.J. (1987) *Ann. Rev. Biochem.*, **56**, 365–94.
52. Polypeptide ligation occurs during post-translational modification of concanavalin A. Carrington, D.M., Auffret, A. and Hanke, D.E. (1985) *Nature*, **313**, 64–7.
53. Post-translational processing of concanavalin A precursors in jackbean cotyledons. Bowles, D.J., Marcus, S.E., Pappin, D.J.C., *et al* (1986) *J. Cell Biol.*, **102**, 1284–97.
54. New way of protein maturation. Sharon, N. and Lis, H. (1986) *Nature*, **323**, 203–4.
55. Production of pea lectin in *Escherichia coli.* Stubbs, M.E., Carver, J.P. and Dunn, R.J. (1986) *J. Biol. Chem.*, **261**, 6141–4.
56. Expression of ricin A chain in *Escherichia coli.* O'Hare, M., Roberts, L.M., Thorpe, P.E., *et al* (1987) *FEBS Lett.*, **216**, 73–8.
57. Soybean seed lectin gene and flanking nonseed protein genes are developmentally regulated in transformed tobacco plants. Okamuro, J.K., Jofuku, K.D. and Goldberg, R.B. (1986) *Proc. Natl. Acad. Sci. USA*, **83**, 8240–4.
58. Differences in expression between two seed lectin alleles obtained from normal and

lectin-deficient beans are maintained in transgenic tobacco. Voelker, T., Sturm, A. and Chrispeels, M.J. (1987) *EMBO J.*, **6**, 3571–7.

59. The ultrastructural visualization of cell surface glycoconjugates. Bayer, E.A., Skutelsky, E. and Wilchek, M. (1982) *Meth. Enzymol.*, **83**, 195–215.

59a. Altered glycosylation is induced in both α- and β-subunits of chorionic gonadotropin produced by choriocarinoma. Endo, T., Nishimura, R., Muchizuki, M. *et al* (1988) *J. Biochem. (Japan)*, **103**, 1035–38.

60. Fractionation and structural assessment of oligosaccharides and glycopeptides by the use of immobilized lectin. Osawa, T. and Tsuji, T. (1987) *Ann. Rev. Biochem.*, **56**, 21–42.

61. Systematic fractionation of oligosaccharides of human immunoglobulin G by serial affinity chromatography on immobilized lectin columns. Harada, H., Kamei, M., Tokumoto, Y. *et al* (1987) *Anal. Biochem.*, **164**, 374–81.

62. Detection of gangliosides that bind cholera toxin: direct binding of ^{125}I-labelled toxin to thin-layer chromatograms. Magnani, J.L., Smith, D.F. and Ginsburg, V. (1980) *Anal. Biochem.*, **109**, 399–402.

63. The glycolipid specificity of *Erythrina cristagalli* agglutinin. Ehrlich-Rogozinski, S., De Maio, A., Lis, H. and Sharon, N. (1987) *Glycoconjugate J.*, **4**, 379–90.

64. Lectin affinity high-performance liquid chromatography columns for the resolution of nucleotide sugars. Harada, H., Kamei, M., Yui, S. and Koyama, F. (1986) *J. Chromatogr.*, **355**, 291–5.

65. Lectin affinity chromatography of glycopeptides. Merkle, R.K. and Cummings, R.D. (1987) *Meth. Enzymol.*, **138**, 232–59.

66. Localization of binding sites for purified *Escherichia coli* P fimbriae in the human kidney. Korhonen, T.K., Virkola, R. and Holthofer, H. (1986) *Infect. Immun.*, **54**, 328–32.

67. Comparison of T-antigen expression in normal, premalignant, and malignant human colonic tissue using lectin and antibody immunohistochemistry. Yuan, M., Itzkowitz, S.H., Boland, *et al* (1986) *Cancer Res.*, **46**, 4841–7.

68. Lectin histochemistry and ultrastructure of kidneys from patients with I-cell disease. Castagnaro, M., Alroy, J., Ucci, A.A. and Jaffe, R. (1987) *Arch. Pathol. Lab. Med.*, **111**, 285–90.

69. Characterization by lectin binding of the sugar moiety of glycocompounds stored in inherited diseases. Lageron, A. (1987) *Histochem. J.*, **19**, 419–25.

70. Biology of disease. Lectin cytochemistry and histochemistry. Damjanov, I. (1987) *Lab. Invest.*, **57**, 5–20.

71. Plant lectins and bacterial toxins as tools for tracing neuronal connections. Sawchenko, P.E. and Gerfen, C.R. (1985) *Trends NeuroSci.*, **8**, 378–84.

72. Heterogeneity of human natural killer (NK) cells: enrichment of NK by negative-selection with the lectin from *Erythrina cristagalli.* Harris, D.T., Iglesias, J.L., Argov, S., Toomey, J. and Koren, H.S. (1987) *J. Leuk. Biol.*, **42**, 163–70.

73. Intravascular haemolysis and renal failure in a patient with T polyagglutination. Levene, C., Sela, R., Blat, J., Friedlaender, M. and Manny, N. (1986) *Transfusion*, **26**, 243–5.

74. Graft-versus-host disease and graft rejection: competing factors in bone marrow transplantation. Reisner, Y. (1987) in: *Progress in Bone Marrow Transplantation* (eds R.P. Gale and R. Champlin), UCLA Symposium on Molecular and Cellular Biology, New Series, Vol. 53, Alan R. Liss, New York, pp. 175–83.

75. Graft-versus-host disease prevention in allogeneic bone marrow transplantation from histocompatible siblings: a pilot study using immunotoxins for T cell depletion of donor bone marrow. Filipovich, A.H., Vallera, D.A., Youle, R.J., Haake, *et al* (1987) *Transplantation*, **44**, 62–9.

76. Glycosylation mutants and the functions of mammalian carbohydrates. Stanley, P. (1987) *Trends Genetics*, **3**, 77–81.
77. Biochemical characterization of animal cell glycosylation mutants. Stanley, P. (1987) *Meth. Enzymol.*, **138**, 443–58.
78. Topography of glycosylation in the rough endoplasmic reticulum and Golgi apparatus. Hirschberg, C.B. and Snider, M.D. (1987) *Ann. Rev. Biochem.*, **56**, 63–87.
79. Tumor cell surface carbohydrates and the metastatic phenotype. Dennis, J.W. and Laferte, S. (1987) *Cancer Metast. Rev.*, **5**, 185–204.
80. $\beta 1 \rightarrow 6$ Branching of Asn-linked oligosaccharides is directly associated with metastasis. Dennis, J.W., Laferté, S., Waghorne, C., Breitman, M.L. and Kerbel, R.S. (1987) *Science*, **236**, 582–5.
81. The lectins: their present status. Boyd, W.C. (1963) *Vox Sang.*, **8**, 1–32.
82. Distribution and function of plant lectins. Etzler, M.E. (1986) in reference 1, pp. 371–435.
83. Endogenous lectins from cultured soybean cells: isolation of a protein immunologically cross-reactive with seed soybean agglutinin and analysis of its role in binding of *Rhizobium japonicum*. Ho, S.-C., Malek-Hedayat, S., Wang, J.L. and Schindler, M. (1986) *J. Cell Biol.*, **103**, 1043–54.
84. Recognition of *Rhizobium trifolii* by the white clover lectin trifoliin A. Dazzo, F.B., Hollingsworth, R.I., Philip *et al* (1986) in *Molecular Biology of Seed Storage Proteins and Lectins* (eds L.M. Shannon and M.J. Chrispeels), American Society of Plant Physiologists, Rockville, Maryland, pp. 45–52.
85. Plant seed lectins disrupt growth of germinating fungal spores. Brambl, R. and Gade, W. (1985) *Physiol. Plant.*, **64**, 402–8.
86. Plant chitinases are potent inhibitors of fungal growth. Schlumbaum, A., Mauch, F., Vogeli, U. and Boller, T. (1986) *Nature*, **324**, 365–7.
87. Trafficking of lysosomal enzymes in normal and disease states. Kornfeld, S. (1986) *J. Clin. Invest.*, **77**, 1–6.
88. Potential role of cell surface lectin in lymphocyte recirculation. Rosen, S.D. and Stoolman, L.M. (1987) in reference 5, pp. 152–81.
89. *In vitro* homing of haemopoietic stem cells is mediated by a recognition system with galactosyl and mannosyl specificities. Aizava, S. and Tavassoli, M. (1987) *Proc. Natl Acad. Sci. USA*, **84**, 4485–9.
90. Endogenous galactoside-binding lectins: a new class of functional tumor cell surface molecules related to metastasis. Raz, A. and Lotan, R. (1987) *Cancer Metast. Rev.*, **6**, 433–52.
91. Endogenous lectins in tumors and the immune system. Gabius, H.-J. (1987) *Cancer Invest.*, **5**, 39–46.
92. Involvement of membrane sugar receptors and membrane glycoconjugate in the adhesion of 3LL cell subpopulation to cultured pulmonary cells. Kieda, C. and Monsigny, M. (1986) *Invas. Metast.*, **6**, 347–66.
93. Selective expression of endogenous lactose-binding lectins and lactoseries glycoconjugates in subsets of rat sensory neurons. Regan, L.J., Dodd, J., Barondes, S.H. and Jessell, T.M. (1986) *Proc. Natl Acad. Sci. USA*, **83**, 2248–52.
94. The biology and chemistry of fertilization. Wassarman, P.M. (1987) *Science*, **235**, 553–60.
95. Humoral and cell membrane-associated lectins from invertebrates and lower chordates: specificity, molecular characterization and their structural relationships with putative recognition molecules from vertebrates. Vasta, G.R. and Marchalonis, J.J. (1985) *Dev. Comp. Immunol.*, **9**, 531–9.
96. Immunological significance of invertebrate lectins. Vasta, G.R. and Marchalonis, J.J.

(1984) in: *Recognition Proteins, Receptors and Probes: Invertebrates* (ed. E. Cohen), Allan R. Liss, New York, pp.177–91.

97. Measurement of *Sarcophaga peregrina* lectin under various physiological conditions by radioimmunoassay. Komano, H., Nozawa, R., Mizuno, D. and Natori, S. (1983) *J. Biol. Chem.*, **258**, 2143–7.

98. Purification of a lectin from the haemolymph of Chinese oak silk moth (*Antheraea pernyi*) pupae. Qu, X-M., Zhang, C.-F., Komano, H. and Natori, S. (1987) *J. Biochem.*, **101**, 545–51.

99. Lectins in cellular slime molds. Barondes, S.H. (1986) in reference 1, pp. 467–91.

100. An endogenous lectin and an oligosaccharide participate in adhesion mechanisms in *Dictyostelium*. Barondes, S.H. and Springer, W.R. (1987) in: *Genetic Regulation of Development*, Alan R. Liss, New York, pp. 129–40.

101. Bacterial lectins, cell–cell recognition and infectious disease. Sharon, N. (1987) *FEBS Lett.*, **217**, 1–13.

102. Type 2 fimbrial lectin-mediated phagocytosis of oral *Actinomyces* spp. by polymorphonuclear leukocytes. Sandberg, A.L., Mudrick, L.L., Cisar, *etal* (1986) *Infect. Immun.*, **54**, 472–6.

103. Lectinophagocytosis: a molecular mechanism of recognition between cell surface sugars and lectins in the phagocytosis of bacteria. Ofek, I. and Sharon. N. (1988) *Infect. Immun.*, **56**, 539–47.

APPENDIX A
Molecular properties of some purified lectins

Lectin	Abbreviated name	Molecular weight (Da)	Subunit, molecular weight (Da)	Molecular formula	Carbohydrate, %	Specificity	
						Sugar	Blood type
Chicken liver		$(26\,000)_6$	α26 000	α_6		GlcNAc	–
Concanavalin A	Con A	106 000	α26 500	α_4	0	α-Man	–
Datura stramonium		86 000	α40 000 β46 000	$\alpha\beta$	40	$(GlcNAc)_2$	–
Dolichos biflorus		110–120 000	α27 300 β27 700	$\alpha_2\beta_2$	4	GalNAc	A_1
Erythrina cristagalli		56 800	α26 000 β28 000	$\alpha\beta$	4.5	Gal/GalNAc	–
Fava bean	Favin	52 500	α 5 500 β20 700	$\alpha_2\beta_2$	3	Man	–
Griffonia simplicifolia I		114 000	α32 000 β33 000	$\alpha_4; \beta_4$*	9	Gal; GalNAc	A; B
Griffonia simplicifolia II		113 000	α30 000	α_4	4	GlcNAc	–
Helix pomatia		79 000	α13 000	α_6	8	GalNAc	A

Lentil		46 000	α 5 700 β17 000	$\alpha_2\beta_2$	0	Man	–
Lima bean		$(62\,000)_{2or4}$	α31 000	α_4 or α_8	3–5	GalNAc	A
Pea		50 000	α 5 700 β17 000	$\alpha_2\beta_2$	0	Man	–
Peanut	PNA	110 000	α27 000	α_4	0	Gal	–
Potato		100 000	α50 000	α_2	50	$(GlcNAc)_2$	–
Rabbit liver		$(256\,000)_n$	α48 000 β40 000	$\alpha_2\beta_4$	14	Gal	–
Red kidney bean	PHA	126 000	α31 000 β31 000	$\alpha_4\beta_4$*	10	†	–
Ricinus communis							
agglutinin	RCA I	120 000	α29–31 000 β34–37 000	$\alpha_2\beta_2$	12	Gal	–
toxin	Ricin or RCA II	63 000	α29–33 000 β34 000	αβ		Gal	–
Soybean	SBA	120 000	α30 000	α_4	6.2	GalNAc	–
Wheat germ	WGA	43 200	α21 600	α_2	0	GlcNAc, NeuAc	–

*Molecules consisting of mixtures of α and β subunits in varying proportions also occur.
†See Table 5.1.

APPENDIX B

Systematic and common names

Systematic name	Common name
Plants	
Abrus precatorius	Jequirity bean
Agaricus bisporus	Common mushroom
Arachis hypogaea	Peanut
Canavalia ensiformis	Jack bean
Datura stramonium	Thorn apple (or Jimson weed)
Dolichos biflorus	Horse gram
Erythrina cristagalli	Coral tree
Galanthus nivalis	Snow drop
Glycine max	Soy bean
Hordeum vulgare	Barley
Lathyrus odoratus	Sweet pea
Lens culinaris (syn. *esculenta*)	Lentil
Lotus tetragonolobus	Asparagus pea
Lycopersicon esculenta	Tomato
Mollucella laevis	Irish bell
Phaseolus lunatus (syn. *limensis*)	Lima bean
Phaseolus vulgaris	Kidney bean
Phytolacca americana	Pokeweed
Pisum sativum	Pea
Ricinus communis	Castor bean
Sambucus nigra	Elderberry
Solanum tuberosum	Potato
Triticum vulgare	Wheat
Ulex europaeus	Gorse (or furze)
Vicia cracca	Common vetch
Vicia faba	Fava bean
Vicia villosa	Hairy vetch
Animals	
Allomyrina dichotoma	Beetle
Anguilla anguilla	Eel
Electrophorus electricus	Electric eel
Helix pomatia	Garden snail
Homarus americanus	Lobster
Limax flavus	Slug
Limulus polyphemus	Horseshoe crab
Periplaneta americana	Cockroach
Rana castebaiena	Frog
Sarcophaga perigrina	Flesh fly

Index

Abrin 6, 9, 22
  cytotoxicity 33, 34
  molecular properties 34, 49
Abrus precatorius 6
  agglutinin 22, 49
  toxin, *see* Abrin
N-Acetylgalactosamine 20, 34, 39, 41
  as blood group determinant 14, 42
  lectins specific for 2, 3, 13, 22–4, 38, 49
N-Acetylglucosamine 20, 25, 39, 41, 72, 100
  glycoconjugates 51, 52, 70, 81
  lectins specific for 2, 3, 22, 24, 42, 56, 101
  oligomers 24, 25, 42, 49, 100
  transferase 75, 76, 93, 96
N-Acetyllactosamine 74, 81, 96
N-Acetylneuraminic acid 27, 38, 41, 42, 70
  cell surfaces 88
  lectins specific for 2, 3, 23, 24, 64
Actinomyces 23, 58, 105
Affinity chromatography 75
  glycopeptides 70, 73
  glycoproteins 70–3
  lectins 17, 24, 25
  oligosaccharides 70, 73
Agaricus bisporus lectin 22, 42, 43
Agglutination 1, 2, 6, 17, 21, 26, 27, 69, 85–7, 89
  see also Haemagglutination
Agglutinins, *see individual lectins*
Agrawal, B.B.L. 17
AIDS 88, 89
Ainsworth, C.F. 18
Amino acid sequences, *see* Structure, primary
  see also individual lectins
Amoeba lectin 3, 23, 105
Anguilla anguilla lectin, *see* Eel lectins
Anguilla rostrata lectin, *see* Eel lectins
Antibodies 1, 11, 32, 37, 38, 85, 90
  anti-lectin 9, 55, 70, 102
Arabinose 47, 51, 52, 55
Arachis hypogaea lectin, *see* Peanut agglutinin
Ashwell, G. 18
Asialofetuin 102
Asialoglycoproteins 101
Association constants 37, 38, 43
Aub, J.C. 16

Bacillus anthracis 87
Bacteria
  adherence 4, 105
  binding of lectins to 36
  lectins 52, 58, 105
Barker, B. 15, 16
Barley lectin 49, 55
Bauhinia purpurea lectin 43
Beetle lectin 3, 29
Binding sites
  carbohydrate 34, 37, 42, 47, 54–6, 59–61, 63, 64
  see also Metal ions
Biosynthesis 65–8
Bird, G.W.G. 13
Blood group(s) 74
  determinants 14, 45
  lectins specific for 11–13, 23, 42, 87
  typing 87
Bone marrow transplantation 89, 90
Boyd, W.C. 11, 13

Brain 84
Burger, M.M. 17

Canavalia ensiformis, see Jack bean lectin, *see* Concanavalin A
Cancer 16, 32, 81, 82, 84
  see also Leukaemia; Malignant cells; Metastasis
Cancer antennarius lectin 42
Carbohydrate specificity 9, 20
  aromatic glycosides 40
  monosaccharides 2
  oligosaccharides 39, 40, 42–6
see also individual lectins and saccharides
Carbohydrate units
  N-linked 43, 45, 51, 73, 81, 93, 94, 96, 101
  O-linked 43, 95, 96, 103
Castor bean, *see* Ricin
Cell fractionation 15, 27, 85, 86, 89
Cell migration 101
Cell surface 26
  carbohydrates 10, 14, 77, 79, 81, 93, 95, 99
  receptors 33
  see also Membranes
Cells
  baby hamster kidney 93
  Chinese hamster ovary 93, 96
  haemocytes 23
  hepatocytes 22, 56, 101, 105
  intestinal 105
  Kupffer 22
  lectin resistant 92, 93, 94, 95, 96
  polymorphonuclear leukocytes 105
  see also Erythrocytes; Lymphocytes; Macrophages
Cereal lectins 21, 54
Chromosome analysis 15, 89
Clover lectin 99
Cockroach lectin 3
Combining sites, *see* Binding sites
Concanavalin A 10, 18, 61, 70, 89, 95, 100
  amino acid sequence 53, 54
  applications
    glycoconjugate research 70, 72, 73, 75, 76, 80
    histochemistry 80, 81, 83
    immunology 88, 90, 91
    microbiology 87
  binding site 59
  biosynthesis 65, 66
  carbohydrate specificity 20, 38–42, 45
  cell binding 77
  cytotoxicity 33, 93
  enhancement of phagocytosis 33
  gene cloning 65
  induction of lymphocyte cytotoxicity 32
  insulin-like activity 33
  maligant cell detection 81
  metal binding 17, 50
  mitogenic activity 16, 28, 29
  purification 17, 25
  structure, three-dimensional 59–61
  subunits 47, 66
Cucumber lectin 21

Datura stramonium lectin 39, 47, 49, 52, 55
Dictyostelium discoideum lectin, *see* Slime mold lectin; Discoidin
Dictyostelium purpureum lectin, *see* Slime mold lectin
Dioclea grandiflora lectin 53
Discoidin 104
DNA 30, 32, 52, 65
Dolichos biflorus
  leaf lectin 22
  seed lectin 3, 84
    applications 77, 83, 84, 88
    blood type specificity 13, 87
    carbohydrate specificity 39
    gene cloning 67
    purification 25

Edelman, G.M. 17
Eel lectins
  serum 3, 22, 87
  tissue 3, 22, 56
Ehrlich, P. 6, 8, 9
Elderberry lectin 3, 22, 39
Electrophorus electricus lectin, *see* Eel lectins
Endoplasmic reticulum 65, 80, 81
Entamoeba histolytica, see Amoeba
Enterobacteria 23
  see also individual organisms
Erythrina cristagalli lectin 3
  applications 74, 75, 77, 86
  carbohydrate specificity 20, 39, 74
  carbohydrate units of 51

mitogenic activity 29
purification 24
Erythrocytes 74, 85, 88, 103
modification 20, 27
see also Blood groups; Haemagglutination
Escherichia coli 58, 68
infection by 105
lectin 3, 23, 41, 42

Farnes, P. 15, 16
Fava bean lectin 3
amino acid sequence 53, 54, 61
biosynthesis 65
carbohydrate specificity 41
gene cloning 65
molecular properties 47
three-dimensional structure 60
Fertilization 103
Fimbriae 23, 58, 79, 105
Flesh fly lectin 3, 103
Food, lectins in 34, 35
Frog lectin 3
Fucoidin 101
Fucose 20, 38, 41, 42, 101
as blood group determinant 14
glycoconjugates 51, 52, 94
lectins specific for 2, 3, 13, 22, 56
Fucosidase 78, 83
Functions
carbohydrates 51, 95, 96
lectins 97, 98
invertebrates 103, 104
microorganisms 104–7
plants 100
vertebrates 100–103
viruses 107
Fungi 100

Galα4Gal 58, 79
Galβ3GalNAc 88
Galβ4GlcNAc, *see N*-Acetyllactosamine
Galactosamine 38
Galactose 20, 63
cell surface 102, 105
glycoconjugates 51, 52, 55, 70, 81, 95, 102
lectins specific for 2, 3, 22, 24, 38, 41, 49, 56, 101, 102, 104
Galactosidase 78

Gallo, R.C. 16
Garden snail lectin 3
see also Helix pomatia lectin
Giardia lamblia lectin 24
Glucose 38, 40, 41
Glycine max, see Soybean agglutinin
Glycoconjugates 69, 76, 95
see also Glycoproteins; Glycolipids; Proteoglycans
Glycolipids 26, 74, 95
N-Glycolylneuraminic acid 42
Glycopeptides 43, 45, 70, 73, 74
Glycophorin 70
Glycoproteins 33, 50
affinity chromatography 17, 70, 71
biosynthesis 79—81, 93–5
clearance 18, 101
detection by lectins 70
intracellular traffic 101
precipitation 20, 37
Glycosidases 74, 79, 93
see also individual enzymes
Glycosphingolipids, *see* Glycolipids
Glycosylation, *see* Glycoproteins, biosynthesis
Goldstein, I.J. 17
Golgi apparatus 79, 81, 95, 101
Gottschalk, A. 18
Griffonia simplicifolia 3, 12, 22
leaf lectin 22
lectin I
applications 75, 77–9
blood group specificity 87
carbohydrate specificity 40
induction of macrophage cytotoxicity 32, 33
isolectins 49
lectin II 96
lectin IV 45, 46

Haemagglutination 2, 10, 15, 20, 37
Haemolymph 23
Hapten inhibition 2, 37
Hardman, K. 18
Hare, R. 18
Heart lectin
calf 22, 25
Helix pomatia lectin 30, 69
applications 74, 81–3, 87, 88
blood group specificity 23, 87

carbohydrate specificity 42
purification 25
Hepatic binding protein 18
see also Liver lectin
Hirst, G.K. 18
Homarus americanus lectin 29
Homologies
animal lectins 56, 57
bacterial lectins 58
circular 54, 65
legume lectins 53, 54, 66, 67
Horseshoe crab lectin, *see Limulus polyphemus* lectin
Howell, S.F. 9
Human chorionic gonadotropin 73

I cell disease 101
Immunoglobulin production 30
Immunology 1, 6, 9, 88, 90
see also Antibodies
Immunotoxins 34, 90
Infection 105–7
Influenza virus lectin 3
carbohydrate specificity 18, 24, 42
in infection 107
three-dimensional structure 63, 64
Insulin 33
Interferon 30
Interleukins 30, 32
Invertebrate lectins 23, 50, 57, 58, 103
Isolectins 47, 48, 49, 50, 54, 61

Jack bean 3, 10
lectin, *see* Concanavalin A

Kidney 79
Kidney bean lectin, *see* PHA
Kidney beans 34, 35
Klebsiella pneumoniae lectin 3, 105

Lactose 63, 64
Landsteiner, K. 10
Lectin derivatives 69, 85
Lectin genes
cloning 66
expression in plants 67, 68
see also individual lectins
Lectin resistance 93–5
Lectinophagocytosis 105–7
Legume lectins 12, 21, 47, 52, 53, 60, 65, 98
see also individual lectins
Lens culinaris lectin, *see* Lentil lectin
Lentil lectin 3
amino acid sequence 53
applications 76
carbohydrate specificity 41, 42
cytotoxicity 93
mitogenic activity 29
molecular properties 47
Leukaemia 90
Li, J.G. 14
Lima bean lectin 3, 12, 13, 87
Limulus polyphemus lectin 3, 23, 47, 50, 69
Liver lectin
chicken 3, 22, 42, 56, 57
rabbit 3, 22, 29, 56, 101
rat 3, 22
Lobster lectin 3, 29
Lotus tetragonolobus lectin 3, 77
blood type specificity 12, 87
carbohydrate specificity 13, 40
Lung lectin
calf 22
human 56
rat 42
Lymphocytes 27, 29, 30, 77, 91
cytotoxic 32
fractionation 86
migration 101
stimulation, *see* Mitogens
Lymphokines 30
Lysosomes 83, 101

Mäkelä, O. 12
Macrophages 32, 33, 56, 101–4
Malignant cells 16, 17, 81
Malignant transformation 17, 27
Mammalian lectins 3, 18, 50, 101
Mannose 20, 38, 39, 41
glycoconjugates 51, 70
lectins specific for 2, 3, 40, 41, 56, 101
Mannose-6-phosphate 57, 101
Melanoma 102
Membranes 72
intracellular 22, 79
lectins of 22, 52, 56, 100
see also Cell surface
Metal ions 50, 54, 58–61
Metastasis 81, 83, 96, 102
Micrococcus luteus 33

Mitogens 28, 29, 49
  applications 88–91
  mechanism of action 30–32
Modeccin 34
Moluccella laevis lectin 87
Morell, A.G. 18
Morgan, W.J.T. 13, 14
Mushroom lectin, *see Agaricus bisporus* lectin
Mycoplasma gallisepticum 3

Neisseria gonorrhoeae 87
Neoglycoproteins 102
Neuroanatomy 84, 85
Neurons 102
Nowell, P.C. 14, 15
Nuclear magnetic resonance 45, 74

Oligomannose 43
Oligosaccharides 43, 45, 74, 75
  see also Carbohydrate units
Osgood, E.E. 14
Ovalbumin 71, 73

Pea lectin 3, 66, 94
  amino acid sequence 53
  biosynthesis 65, 66
  carbohydrate specificity 41, 42
  gene cloning 68
  mitogenic activity 29
  molecular properties 47
  purification 25
  subunits 47
  three-dimensional structure 60
Peanut agglutinin 3, 50
  applications
    blood banks 87, 88
    cell fractionation 85, 88, 89
    cyto- and histochemistry 77, 78, 79, 83
    glycoconjugate research 70
  carbohydrate specificity 39
  haemagglutination by 21, 27
  inhibition of fungal growth 100
  malignant cell detection 81, 83
  purification 25
Peroxidase, horseradish 69, 70, 85
PHA 51, 68, 89, 95
  amino acid sequence 53
  applications
    cell fractionation 15, 85
    immunology 88
    neuroanatomy 85
  carbohydrate specificity 39, 42
  cytotoxicity 93
  gene cloning 66–8
  in cell fractionation 85
  isolectins 49
  mitogenic activity 14, 15, 28, 29
  nutritional aspects 36
  subunits 49, 66
Phagocytosis 33
  see also Lectinophagocytosis
Phaseolus lunatus lectin, *see* Lima bean lectin
Phaseolus vulgaris lectin, *see* PHA
Phytohaemagglutinin, *see* PHA
Pili, *see* Fimbriae
Pisum sativum lectin, *see* Pea lectin
Placenta lectin 3
PNA, *see* Peanut agglutinin
Pokeweed mitogen 15, 16, 22, 29, 88
Polyagglutination 88
Polysaccharide precipitation 20, 37
Potato lectin 21, 22
  carbohydrate units of 47, 51, 52
  inhibition of fungal growth 100
  molecular properties 55
  purification 25
Precipitation, *see* Glycoproteins, Polysaccharides
Proteoglycans 95
Protozoa 23
Pseudomonas aeruginosa lectins 3, 23, 29

Raubitschek, H. 9, 10
Receptors 71
Recognition, role of lectins in 18, 97
Red kidney bean lectin, *see* PHA
Reguera, R. M. 11
Renkonen, K. O. 11, 12
Rhizobia 98, 99
Ricin 6, 9
  applications 85, 90
  cytotoxicity 33, 34, 93
  gene cloning 68
  molecular properties 34, 49, 50
  three-dimensional structure 62, 63
Ricinus communis 3, 6
  agglutinin 22, 68
    applications 75, 76, 81

carbohydrate specificity 40, 43
gene cloning 67
molecular properties 49, 50
purification 25
toxin, *see* Ricin
RNA 34, 52, 76
Robinia pseudoacacia lectin 22, 33
Rye lectin 49, 55

Sachs, L. 17
Salmonellae 23
Salvia sclarea lectin 87
Sanfoin 53
Sarcophaga peregrina lectin 32, 58
Sea urchin lectin 3, 57
Sela, B.A. 17
Sendai virus 24, 96
Shapley, E. 13
Sialic acid 38, 95
cell surfaces 83, 102, 107
glycoconjugates 70
lectins specific for 23, 39, 42
see also N-Acetylneuraminic acid; N-Glycolylneuraminic acid
Sialidase 29, 88–107
Silk moth lectin 103
Sindbis virus 95, 96
Slime mold lectin 3, 29, 104
see also Discoidin
Slug lectin 3
Snake venom lectin 3
Snowdrop lectin 22, 41
Solanaceae lectins 47, 52, 55
Sophora japonica
leaf lectin 22
seed lectin 30, 51
Soybean agglutinin 3, 21, 100
amino acid sequence 53, 54
applications
bone marrow transplantation 89
cell fractionation 85, 86
glycoconjugate research 74, 75
microbiology 87
biosynthesis 66
carbohydrate specificity 20, 43
carbohydrate units of 51
gene cloning 67, 68
malignant cell detection 81, 83
mitogenic activity 17
nutritional aspects 36

Specificity
blood type 11–13, 23, 42, 87
carbohydrate 37–46
species 10, 11
Staphylococcus albus 33
Staphylococcus aureus 33
Stillmark, H. 6, 8
Stinging nettle 47
Streptococcus sanguis 104
Structure
primary 52–8
see also Homologies
three-dimensional 59–67
Subunits of lectins 1, 47, 58
Sumner, J.B. 9
Symbiosis 98–100

T antigen 88
Thymocytes 77, 85, 102
Thymus 78, 79, 102
Tomato lectin 21, 22, 51
carbohydrate units of 47
nutritional aspects 35
Toxicity 6, 32–4, 92
Trifoliin 99
Tumour, *see* Cancer

UDP 76
Ulex europaeus lectin 3, 21, 77–9, 81, 83, 84, 87

Vertebrate lectins 52, 56, 58, 101, 102
Vesicular stomatitis virus 95, 96
Vibrio cholerae lectin 3
Vicia cracca lectin 12, 22, 87
Vicia faba, see Fava bean lectin
Vicia graminea lectin
applications 88
blood type specificity 13, 87
carbohydrate specificity 39, 42
carbohydrate unit 51
Vicia villosa lectin 39, 42, 81
Viruses, *see individual entries*
Viscumin 34
Volkensin 34

Watkins, W.M. 13, 14
Wheat 3, 49
Wheat germ agglutinin 50, 72, 94, 100
amino acid sequence 54, 62

applications
  glycoconjugate research 70, 71, 73
  histochemistry 81, 83
  microbiology 87
  neuroanatomy 85
carbohydrate specificity 20, 39, 42
cytotoxicity 33, 93
enhancement of phagocytosis 33
induction of macrophage cytotoxicity 32
inhibition of fungal growth 100
insulin-like activity 33
isolectins 48, 54, 61
malignant cell detection 17, 81, 96
  molecular properties 47
  nutritional aspects 35
  purification 25
  subunits 48, 54, 55
  three-dimensional structure 61, 62
Wistaria floribunda mitogen 29

X-Ray crystallography, *see* Structure, three-dimensional; *individual lectins*
Xylose 51

Yeasts 33, 87, 101